GEOGRAPHERS

and what they do

AIRMEN AND WHAT THEY DO,
  BY *Charles I. Coombs*
ARCHEOLOGISTS AND WHAT THEY DO,
  BY *Robert J. Braidwood*
THE CLERGY AND WHAT THEY DO,
  BY *Hartzell Spence*
CONSERVATIONISTS AND WHAT THEY DO,
  BY *C. William Harrison*
DOCTORS AND WHAT THEY DO,
  BY *Harold Coy*
ENGINEERS AND WHAT THEY DO,
  BY *Harold Coy*
FORESTERS AND WHAT THEY DO,
  BY *John Perry and Jane Greverus Perry*
FOREST FIRE FIGHTERS AND WHAT THEY DO,
  BY *C. William Harrison*
MARINES AND WHAT THEY DO,
  BY *Karl Schuon and Earl Smith*
NAVY MEN AND WHAT THEY DO,
  BY *Cmdr. Herbert J. Gimpel, USN*
NEWS REPORTERS AND WHAT THEY DO,
  BY *David Botter*
NUCLEAR SUBMARINE SKIPPERS
AND WHAT THEY DO,
  BY *Cmdr. George P. Steele, USN, and Cmdr. Herbert J. Gimpel, USN*
POLITICIANS AND WHAT THEY DO,
  BY *David Botter*
ROCKETMEN AND WHAT THEY DO,
  BY *Charles I. Coombs*
SERVICEWOMEN AND WHAT THEY DO,
  BY *Karl Schuon and Ronald D. Lyons*
SOLDIERS AND WHAT THEY DO,
  BY *Col. Arthur Symons, USAR*

GEOGRAPHERS

and

what

they

do

William Warntz, Ph. D.

The American Geographical Society

Franklin Watts, Inc.
575 Lexington Avenue, New York 22

Quotations from Harold Gatty on pages 102, 117, Chapter 6, are from his book, *Nature Is Your Guide*, published by E. P. Dutton & Co. Inc., New York, 1957. Quoted by permission from the publisher.

SECOND PRINTING

Library of Congress Catalog Card Number: 64–11916
© Copyright 1964 by Franklin Watts, Inc.
Printed in the United States of America

Acknowledgment

The author wishes to express his thanks to the American Geographical Society of New York and especially to Mrs. Wilma B. Fairchild, Editor of that society's quarterly journal, the *Geographical Review,* for permission to reprint here in Chapter 4 parts of his article, "Transatlantic Flights and Pressure Patterns." This article in its entirety appeared in 1961 in Volume 51, Number 2, pages 187–212, of the *Geographical Review.*

Similarly, the author is indebted to the editors of *World Politics.* This quarterly journal is under the editorial sponsorship of the Center of International Studies of Princeton University. Permission has been given to the author to use in Chapter 3 of the present book selected passages from his article, "Geography at Mid-Twentieth Century," which appeared in Volume 11, Number 3, 1959, pages 442–454, of *World Politics*.

Recently the author attended a lengthy conference of many scholars concerned with the improvement of courses of study in the Social Sciences and the Humanities under the joint auspices of the American Council of Learned Societies and a division of Educational Services Incorporated. While there, the author had the good fortune to be able to work through again his own views of the essentials of geography as an academic discipline in active cooperation with two distinguished geographers, Dr. William Pattison, now a member of the faculty of San Fernando Valley State College, Northridge, California, and Dr. William Bunge, Wayne State University, Detroit, Michigan. Chapter 3, here, is intended to reflect in part the concluding report of the geographers at that conference. The author hopes he has been able to capture some of the intellectual excitement and broad scope of the ideas pertaining to geography engendered by the presentations of those two able gentlemen at that conference.

Special thanks are owed to Miss Alice Dickinson, editor, Franklin Watts, Inc. Perhaps formal acknowledgment here by the author of his awareness that he made unduly large demands upon Miss Dickinson's store of experience and extraordinarily good judgment in publication matters in general and manuscript revision in particular will be accepted by her as a token of his appreciation. It was truly a most agreeable experience to be able to work in close cooperation with so capable a person.

But, neither Miss Dickinson nor any of the other above persons who offered such generous assistance should be called to task for any of the book's shortcomings or inaccuracies. These are solely the responsibility of the author and doubtless stem from his inability to utilize most fully the advice of others.

Above all, I would like to thank my wife, Minerva, who assisted at all stages in the preparation of the original manuscript.

W. W.

Contents

1

Some Geographers at Work

When the National System of Interstate and Defense Highways in the United States is completed in 1975, it is to consist of 41,000 miles of excellent roads which will help make possible high speeds and low costs for their users. The planning of such a system affects, directly or indirectly, the entire national economy and population, and such planning is certainly a matter for serious concern. Besides the obvious knowledge of civil engineering, much theoretical knowledge is necessary concerning the relationship between transportation and such things as the size and spacing of cities, urban and rural land values, trading areas, the availability and use of resources, and so on.

In 1956, when the federal government passed the

1

legislation needed to make possible this multibillion-dollar highway project, a research fund of over 200 million dollars was established. Those responsible for organizing the research program came quickly to realize that geographers would be especially valuable to them, because the size and spacing of cities, the availability of resources, and the other topics mentioned in the first paragraph above are the very ones that professional geographers in this country have studied especially since World War II. Thus, geographers came to serve their nation well. They had the ability, for example, to analyze transportation networks—using such things as the branch of mathematics known as topology, and the algebra of "linear programming"— and they had the capability of making excellent predictions, based on their growing body of "central place theory" knowledge among other things. Geographers are continuing to make important contributions to this ongoing highway project, and several younger geographers, including Garrison, Berry, Marble, Morrill, Nystuen, and Dacey, have been cited for their efforts.

In other countries, too, geographers have been active in national programs. For example, in Finland the making of a national atlas has been accomplished by the staff of the geography department of Helsinki University. In the Netherlands, geographers have helped plan the settlement patterns for the land reclaimed from the Zuider Zee. In Sweden, geographers have interpreted aerial photographs of inaccessible areas, to help develop a program to regulate rivers in the northern part of that country by means of a series of dams and waterpower plants. In the Soviet Union, geographers have developed planning regions to help organize the productive forces of each area into an overall pattern.

Many other examples from various countries could be added to the above list. Although at the present time the number of professional geographers in the world is small, their importance is growing daily, and increasingly they are being recognized as persons who possess skills valuable to modern living.

In the United States there are now about 2,500 professional geographers, and their number is increasing each year. Annually, about fifty graduate students are awarded the academic degree of Doctor of Philosophy (Ph.D.) in geography, following for each a number of years of successful study in a graduate program at an American college. In addition, there are many more students who obtain the intermediate Master's (M.A.) degree as a terminal degree or as a step on the way to the Doctor of Philosophy degree.

Several decades ago there would have been many fewer graduate degrees obtained in geography in a year, and virtually all of the students receiving those degrees would have themselves become teachers in a school, college, or university. Nowadays many more kinds of opportunities are open to geographers, who are actively sought by businesses, governmental departments, and planning agencies, as well as by educational institutions.

Geography is an extraordinarily comprehensive subject. It deals with the whole earth in general, and with many aspects of the earth and its regions in particular. There are some outsiders who say that geography is too inclusive a subject to be useful or convincing as an academic discipline or a professional specialty. They say that it includes so many different kinds of facts and bits of information that it cannot represent a logical, coherent, and meaningful whole. To this, geographers reply that theirs is a special perspective and that it is the *specific point of view shared by geographers* rather than the great amount of diverse data included that makes geography such an important and entirely consistent subject.

Most geographers nowadays strive for excellence in, and they concentrate on, two phases of their subject. Most geographers have both a *regional specialty* and a *topical specialty*. For example, one geographer may be especially interested in and well qualified to teach about and do research concerning Latin America. This is his regional specialty. His topical specialty might well be the study of climates in general. The lists of regional specialties and topical specialties are long ones indeed, and quite impressive.

Some geographers may make a very small country or even just a part of a country their regional specialty. Each of these specialists knows more about the geography of his small area than anyone else on earth. Oftentimes such persons are of great importance to the nation. They represent a very valuable resource upon which the government, for example, can draw when expert advice is needed. As the nation becomes

4

increasingly engaged in activities with other parts of the world, it is a sustaining comfort to know that there are men and women trained to assist. First one area of the world, then another, is in the news—Antarctica, Vietnam, Kashmir, Ghana, Algeria, Cuba, and so on. One geographer spent a lifetime studying Korea, an area regarded by many people as too remote to be of interest. Then suddenly, with a new turn of world affairs, he found that a great many persons in responsible positions wanted to speak with him about his work, and he soon became regarded as a most valuable geographer.

So it is, too, with topical specialties. One geographer may study political boundary lines; another may turn his abilities toward the study of urban problems. Among the very many other topical specialties that geographers engage in are those related to marketing, agriculture, manufacturing, natural resources, landforms, or cartography. The list here is very long, too.

Of all the professional geographers in the United States, most of them still are engaged in teaching although, as was noted above, other kinds of opportunities are becoming increasingly available for the small crop of new geographers our graduate colleges bring forth each year.

Suppose now, however, that you had actually become a teacher of geography at an American college. More than half of the American geographers do teach. Let's look at some geographers at work there first.

The teaching of geography goes on at every academic level from the elementary school to the graduate schools in universities. More years of training and advanced academic degrees are required for those who wish to teach at the higher academic levels. In general, a Bachelor's degree is required for anyone wishing to teach in an elementary or secondary school, although a Master's degree might also be a requirement for qualifying as a teacher in a high school.

For a college position, a Master's degree may be regarded as the minimum requirement. Increasingly, a Doctor's degree is a necessity for anyone wishing to be considered for a permanent position on a college or university faculty.

Any geographer on the faculty of a college can expect to engage in the normal life of a college instructor or professor. He will lecture, and conduct discussion classes; administer examinations, and grade papers; supervise the special studies of certain undergraduate and graduate students majoring in geography; serve on various faculty committees; act as a faculty adviser to various student activities; and in general lead a full, busy, and interesting life. But his interests and associations will not be confined to his own campus. Not only will he keep in close touch with other geographers, but he undoubtedly will also enjoy professional contacts with many people in other special fields, not only in his own college and other colleges or universities, but also in government and in various public and private enterprises.

Through purposely allotted or volunteered extra

6

time, many geographers on college and university faculties engage in research as well as teaching. Oftentimes the research projects are organized within the geography departments of colleges and universities. Sometimes, however, geographers act as consultants to outside groups.

Entirely apart from teaching, there are other careers for geographers, as has been mentioned. In the United States at present, nearly five hundred geographers work directly for government. To an increasing degree, government agencies at the federal, state, county, and municipal levels are employing geographers. It is the federal government, however, that has the most numerous and most widely differing kinds of tasks requiring the special training and abilities of professional geographers.

Most of the geographers in federal service live and work in or near Washington, D. C., although some work in other parts of the United States, and some are in the foreign service. A few, such as the geographers for the Department of State, travel in foreign countries to represent the United States at a number of important international conferences.

In a recent report, one of the geographers for the Department of State said that since 1958 he has "devoted a substantial part of his time to Law of the Sea matters, including serving as technical adviser on the United States delegation to two Geneva conferences on this subject." Another geographer represented the Department of State on the Technical Antarctic Committee. Besides that, for several years "attention has been focused on Africa where the series of new independent states appearing over the political horizon raises problems involving sovereignty, international boundaries, civil, administrative, and even geographic terminology."

Since the end of World War II an extensive worldwide program has been conducted by the Department of State to obtain important and useful maps. This work is carried out principally by geographic attachés assigned to American embassies in such cities as Cairo, Paris, Bonn, Copenhagen, Beirut, New Delhi, and Tokyo. The tasks are organized "on a broad regional basis, consisting of such activities as the purchase of maps; facilitating map exchanges with cartographic agencies of the countries of their responsibilities, as well as keeping apace of cartographic developments in these countries; meeting with mapping officials; and contacting academic institutions and societies. This far-reaching program results in cartographic documentation which can be maintained with current maps and related materials from many parts of the world. Not only the Department of State, but all government agencies concerned with mapping benefit from the items procured."

Geographers are also employed by the Bureau of the Census. It would be virtually impossible to carry out a successful enumeration of the nation's population every ten years if geographers did not utilize and develop maps to help plan for the census, to conduct actual field operations, and to publish the results of the enumeration.

The Bureau of the Census is likely to need more geographers soon, for in the near future there may be a national census every five years instead of every ten. Just recently, Congressional hearings were conducted to ascertain the advisability and practicability of establishing just such a quinquennial census for this country. A number of geographers were called on to offer both spoken and written testimony before the Congressional committee conducting the census hearings.

The Bureau of the Census maintains many interesting records concerning the areal distributions and characteristics of the American people. Included are maps, tables, and atlases summarizing geographical data back all the way to the nation's first census, conducted in 1790, shortly after the establishment of the independent constitutional government. Anyone interested in American history and geography can find much to study here.

A great number of other equally important and professionally satisfying positions held by geographers in the federal government could be described, but perhaps the recent listing by Lloyd D. Black of important offices where one or more professional geographers are actually working will serve to illustrate the part geographers are playing in national affairs at the level of government (see page 132).

Another kind of occupation that has opened up to geographers, especially since World War II, is that of adviser or consultant to any one of various American businesses. The springing up of these opportunities

9

has been occasioned by the rapid expansion of planning and market research activities.

A prominent geographer filling a responsible position with one of the largest American businesses has described the role of American professional geographers in business as falling principally into the following categories: industrial and research; planning; maps and mapping; and editing and publishing.

Geographers in business's industrial and research activities take part in site analyses, market analyses, and the study of regional economics. Industrial site analysts may help decide the use to which industrial land owned by railroads is put. Chain store retailing companies may employ geographers to help select locations for new stores, after careful assembly and examination of information pertaining to expected sales, costs, and profits.

The erection of a large modern integrated iron and steel plant represents an enormous capital outlay. Great care must be exercised to insure the selection of the most profitable location for the plant. A geographer assigned to this task would evaluate carefully a great number of things—including transportation costs of raw materials and fuel, accessibility to markets, labor costs, and pertinent government legislation —before reaching a decision as to where his company's new plant might best be located.

Market analysis is an important aspect of the research engaged in by most large business organizations. Here the geographer helps by his consideration of regional or local differences in customs and tastes.

He thus hopes to evaluate sales potentials in various parts of the country.

Many banks, investment houses, and other financial organizations are interested in the variations in general economic conditions among the different parts of the country. They employ geographers to study these variations, especially when the emphasis is on the current and possible future use of the natural resources of regions.

While much of what is described above can be regarded partly as planning, just as can some of the activities of the government geographers outlined previously, it is also important to note that there are many separate organizations—government bureaus, private groups, and business firms—dedicated solely to planning. Here geographers work on a great many problems and help to make recommendations about urban renewal and slum clearance, new highway systems, recreational land use, and the development of natural resources. Increasingly the problem of the proper conservation of the nation's natural resources occupies geographers' attention.

Some business organizations make maps, globes, and atlases to sell to the general public. Others may work on a contract basis to provide aerial photographs, maps, and charts, for special purposes. In both cases the geographer's long training and experience in cartographic matters make him admirably suited for employment.

Unless the information gained from geographers' research and study can be accurately, attractively, and

11

quickly made available to those who need and want it, much of their work will have been wasted. To insure that the information is properly made available, many people with training and experience in both geography and editing are engaged by publishing houses, research foundations, government agencies, and businesses, to edit and "see through publication" geographical textbooks, monographs, and research reports.

In addition to the academic, government, and business geographers, there is another group, as yet quite small, that is engaged in what might best be called "pure research" in geography. The men in this group are found chiefly in research foundations and non-profit educational institutions, although some universities provide specific opportunities for them. Of course, many geographers in universities, government departments, and businesses also do research, but although some of it might very well be called pure research, most of it is aimed at the solution of certain specific problems and is done in the expectation of an immediate successful application to the tasks at hand. For instance, research may be done with the hope of improving the presentation of a course that a professor offers in a university; or it may be done so that the best possible decision about a new highway's location can be made; or it may involve the designing of a special map projection for navigational purposes.

But, beyond such immediately and obviously utilitarian projects, a certain few geographers have been given the opportunity to carry out research in the kinds of things that interest them most and in which the best of their training, experience, initiative, and imagination can all be combined.

The nature of their pure research is such that for long periods of time there will be no easy indication that progress is being made. To the general public, much of the work would seem involved, intricate, and in defiance of common sense—and much of it is. But someone had faith in these geographers, and has trusted that they will work to the fullest of their abilities and will produce significant results.

While time and again it has been demonstrated that scientific research which at the time of its completion appeared to be quite abstruse and most esoteric later came to have enormously useful applications to new problems, geographers doing pure research do not continue their work because of expectations such as this. They are impelled solely by a curiosity, a love of intellectual endeavor, and a feeling for the importance of philosophical arguments.

As may already have become apparent, much of what geographers do in their professional capacities is intimately bound up with maps. Maps are the most efficient way to show locations and spatial distributions—and it is the relationships among various spatial patterns that geographers study. Geography is at once the art of regional descriptions and the science of spatial relations. A geographer interested in pure research in his subject might well hope to develop the basic principles of regional classification and the major categories of spatial relations. His principal concern

13

will not be just with the unique areas and specific facts he uses to test his hypotheses. Rather, he will be interested in the abstractions and general organizing concepts that can be shown to systematize his subject and that reveal the true nature of geography. It is difficult to make such work clear to a non-geographer, but to a geographer it is wonderfully exciting.

No matter what particular job a new geographer does accept, he undoubtedly will join a professional association by means of which he can maintain contacts with other professional geographers and keep himself informed of developments within his subject. In the United States, this professional organization (the Association of American Geographers) was founded in 1904 and now has approximately two thousand members. It includes representatives from seventeen countries in the Western Hemisphere and twelve in the Eastern Hemisphere. To qualify for full membership, a person must have the doctorate in geography, or an equivalent combination of other degrees and experience, but anyone with a sincere and mature professional interest may become an associate member. The principal objectives of this professional organization are to stimulate geographical research and to improve the application of its results. Meetings, committees, publications, research grants, honor awards, and participation in the work of other scientific groups have all aided in the progress toward these objectives.

The annual meetings are a high point of the organization's activities. There the opportunity occurs to present technical papers and listen to them. Many younger geographers are encouraged to give reports concerning their professional work. The meetings are held in a different part of the country each year, and the local field trips and semisocial occasions that accompany the formal sessions help to bring members into closer contact with one another and to acquaint them firsthand with yet another part of the country.

In addition to this particular professional organization, the Association of American Geographers, there is another one designed particularly for teachers of geography. Many geographers are members of both groups.

Geography is also served by several private societies occupying their own buildings, with permanent staffs to maintain collections of geographic materials, to engage in both applied and original pure research, to promote cartography, to engage in exploration, and to publish books and journals of interest to geographers, other scholars, and the general public.

Varied as the work of geographers may be—in colleges, government, businesses, and research institutions—geographers do have many interests in common, and are influenced to a greater or lesser degree by several strong traditions in geography. These will be considered later.

2

Geographers—from Ancient Times to the Present

Here is a dialogue from the year A.D. 1660:

Examining chaplain: *Quid est fides?*
Isaac Barrow: *Quod non vides.*
Examining chaplain: *Quid est spes?*
Isaac Barrow: *Magna res.*
Examining chaplain: *Quid est caritas?*
Isaac Barrow: *Magna raritas.*

With this last rejoinder by Barrow, the examining chaplain retreated, filled with indignation, to report to his bishop that there was a candidate for ordination to the Anglican priesthood who would respond

16

with nothing but "rhyming answers to moral questions."

The bishop, who knew the pedantry of his chaplain, also knew Barrow by repute and was delighted to learn that good humor and sprightliness could be found in one so learned and inventive in mathematics and science, and inclined to a religious life.

Isaac Barrow was indeed an outstanding mathematician and scientist. Such was his brilliance that he was selected to become the first professor to hold the newly created Lucasian Chair in Mathematics and Natural Philosophy at Trinity College of Cambridge University in England.

Memorable as Barrow's contributions to mathematics were, he is best remembered because it was under him that Isaac Newton, who entered Trinity in 1661, studied mathematics.

Barrow was interested not only in mathematics, but also in theology. He took the ordination examination for the priesthood in the Church of England in 1660 at the age of thirty, with the notion that upon his retirement from the faculty of Cambridge University he might live out his life in the service of his church as one of its ministers. But, so outstanding was his pupil, that Barrow announced that it was Newton, with his incomparable genius, who should be the Lucasian Professor. Barrow retired in 1669, with the recommendation that Newton succeed him. So Barrow became a full-time clergyman at the age of thirty-nine, a long time before he originally had planned to do so.

No ambitious recounting need here be given of Isaac Newton's intellectual accomplishments. It is sufficient only to mention that Newton was distinguished for having developed not only the binomial theorem, and the differential calculus—independently but simultaneously with the German, Leibniz—but especially, the universal laws of gravitation.

But why should Newton and Barrow have a place in a chapter about geographers? the reader may wonder.

Newton's connections with geography—and this is why the preceding stories were related—are twofold. In one case they were immediate to his day, and direct to the discipline of geography. In the other case, the effects were indirect and were delayed in their impact for many centuries. Both of these occurrences are interesting and important to our narrative. The second will be considered later in this book, but the first— the direct one—will be discussed now.

In 1669, when Isaac Newton ascended to the Lucasian Professorship of Mathematics and Natural Philosophy at Cambridge University in England, he was required to lecture once a week during the term on pure mathematics, or on astronomy, geography, optics, or statics, and to provide two hours each week for consultation with his students. In addition, as Lucasian Professor, he was to recommend and supervise the required reading.

Newton decided to organize the geography course for his Cambridge students around the book, *Geographia Generalis,* by Bernhardus Varenius. Varenius had published this work in Latin in Amsterdam. To make it suitable for his students' needs, Newton edited it, enlarged it, improved it, and included special tables. The first Newtonian edition of Varenius' work appeared in Latin in 1672 and was Newton's first publication. For a century, through successive revisions and improvements, and finally through translation by a direct line of descent among Newton's students, the book remained prominent.

Its original author, Bernhard Varen, was born near Hamburg, Germany, in 1622. As was still the custom with scholars of his time, he Latinized his name to Varenius. In 1650, at the time he first published the *Geographia Generalis,* he was only twenty-eight years old, but he had achieved the degree, Doctor of Medicine, in addition to having spent some years in mathematics. He died before the year 1650 was out, and the world lost far too early this geographer-mathematician-physician.

Varenius had decided to write his *Geographia Generalis,* or *General Geography,* because he felt that "special geography"—the purely verbal description of selected places—had come to be treated at tedious length almost to the exclusion of general systematic, or physical, geography. The result of this, he feared, was that the young men of his time, while learning more and more special geography, were largely ignorant of the foundations of the whole study.

According to Varenius, "Geography is that part of *mixed mathematics* which explains the State of the Earth, and of its Parts, depending on Quantity, *viz.*

19

its Figure, Place, Magnitude, and Motion, with Celestial Appearances, etc.

"We divide *Geography* into *General* and *Special*, or *Universal and Particular*. . . . We call that *Universal Geography*, which considers the whole Earth in general, and explains its properties without regard to particular countries. But *Special* or *Particular Geography* describes the Constitution or Situation of each single Country by itself which is two fold, *viz. Chorographical*, which describes Countries of considerable extent; or *Topographical*, which gives a View of some place or small Tract of Earth."

This distinction between general and special is an important one, for geography all through the ages has progressed only when a proper balance between these two equally important aspects has been struck.

The writings of Varenius were the best representatives of a new age of enlightenment in geography. Like many other academic subjects, geography had endured a long and barren period of neglect in Europe. The general intellectual awakening of Varenius' time, greatly spurred on by exploration, discovery, and trade, was attended by many new geographic facts. The stirring interest in geography had brought about the revival of classical geographical presentations, but the spirit of the new age would not be content merely with reference to the old. A Europe in ferment was seeking fresh expression in all aspects of life. New geographic theory was needed to help bring forth order from the welter of recently discovered material. With Varenius' offering, and especially with the impetus given to the work by young Isaac Newton, academic geography came to full stature.

Before taking account of the geographers who followed Varenius, some mention should be made of his earliest predecessors, the geographers of antiquity. From the Greek and Roman worlds there are a great number of these geographers, though in this short space attention can be given to only a few of them.

Today we regard Homer's *Odyssey* as romantic fiction, yet it is more than that. It deals subtly with a wide range of human motives and experiences. Adventure runs high. The *Odyssey* starts with cattle rustling and goes ahead to breathtaking escapes from monsters and one-eyed giants, in last-ditch fights against great odds. Mistaken identities, supernatural mysteries, sorceries, and transformations are described in terms so vivid that their fascination and appeal have not diminished through the ages, and the human qualities portrayed are those of men everywhere.

By all means, read a translation of the *Odyssey* and its companion piece the *Iliad* for the sheer joy and adventure of doing so. Perhaps you have already. Do it again. Whether you are reading the books for the first time or are going to reread them, though, do so also with the idea of finding out what the author's conceptions of the world were. His epics were the bible of the Greeks. In school, boys learned the poems by heart before they went on to the rest of the impressive array of Greek lyric poems and the dramas of tragedy and comedy. Not just the young students, but mature scholars, too, turned from time to time to Homer, not only as the source of Greek legends and stories, but also as the most distinguished authority on geography.

The poetry of Homer dates from about 900 B.C. At this time, the Greeks knew little about the world beyond their own peninsula and the islands and shores of the Aegean Sea. For a few centuries, Homer's descriptions of the world—however fanciful they seem to modern readers—were taken as absolute truth. Then followed a period in which Homer was regarded as having written with precision only about his own country. His accounts of the lands beyond the Aegean were felt surely to have been taken from his imagination alone. In time, however, Homer was again revered as the absolute authority, and attempts were made to establish agreement between places he described and actual spots on the Mediterranean shore.

Homer's geography considered the earth as a flat disk with Greece at the center. Near this center there were seas, with a narrow entrance to the Ocean Stream, which surrounded the land all about. The sun and most of the heavenly constellations, so intertwined with Greek mythology, rose out of the Ocean Stream and sank into it. There were no specific terms for the cardinal directions, except the words for "toward the dawn," or generally eastward, and "toward the darkness," or generally westward. In place of cardinal directions, there were names for four winds, which were regarded as separate, independent, but animated creatures or beings.

From these beginnings the Greeks went on to make many observations about the earth, and their philosophical thinking about our planet, its inhabitants, and their activities was especially brilliant. Not only did they offer careful scientific and mathematical statements, but they gave careful verbal descriptions, as well. In fact, the word "geography" itself comes to us from the Greeks, and refers literally to written descriptions of the earth.

Perhaps the first person to announce description of geographical areas as his principal purpose was Hecataeus, writing around the year 520 B.C. Although his *Description of the Earth* was principally an account of coastal areas, it also included remarks on inland tribes and the Persian Empire as far as the borders of India. Most of Hecataeus' writings were lost, but the fragments that remain, when pieced together with some of his quotations found in other works, provide a valuable geographical document. His knowledge came from personal travel, supplemented by his conversations with traders.

Later, many other similar writings were produced, ranging from tabular presentations of facts about certain areas to vivid descriptions that were admitted blends of fact and fancy. But another type of writing came to prevail. It was a mixture—and a good one— of what we would today call history and geography. Today's geographers and historians both claim as their predecessors the best of the writers in this field. Chief among these ancient Greeks were Herodotus, Thucydides, and Polybius.

Herodotus lived in the fifth century B.C. He was born a subject of the Persians in Asia Minor. He traveled widely over the Greek world, living for a time in Athens and then in Thurii, Italy, where, it is believed, he died when not quite sixty years old. Herodotus wrote of the wars between the Greeks and the Persians, introducing these episodes with long statements of the development of both nations and of all the people with whom they came in contact. His descriptions of the physical environments of nations and his account of how surroundings are related to national activities have stood through the centuries as models for those who later have written of "environmental determinism."

In fact, one might say that Herodotus had such modern views of geography that he was not fully appreciated until the latter part of the nineteenth century A.D. And, while the latter nineteenth-century geographic philosophy is no longer in vogue, both Herodotus and the nineteenth-century geographers still make excellent and provocative reading.

At one time, Herodotus was called the "Father of Lies" because he included myths and legends in his scholarly works. It takes careful study to see that for the most part he did not believe these tall tales but, with an attitude like that of more modern human geographers, included them to reveal the outlook of those peoples of whom he was writing.

Herodotus was interested chiefly in comparisons of different cultures and their physical bases. While thoroughly patriotic to the small Greek city-states, and appreciative of the heroic aspects of their successful war against the Persians, he wrote in no narrow, bigoted spirit. He was able to put Greek culture into proper perspective, to the great advantage of later scholars. It is indeed unfortunate that the world has not had more cultural geographer-historians like Herodotus.

The second member of our set of three Greek geographer-historians was Thucydides, who lived as a younger contemporary of Herodotus. In the spirit of Greek tragedy, he wrote about the Peloponnesian War between Athens and Sparta, revealing the fatal defects that led to the Athenian downfall.

The third of the trio was Polybius, who lived three hundred years later than the other two. He was a man of practical affairs as well as a scholar, and was secretary-general of the Greek city-states when they made their last attempt to form an organization much like the modern United Nations. Polybius saw Greece conquered by Rome. He was one of the hostages sent to Rome after the defeat of Perseus (167 B.C.) in the Third Macedonian War.

Polybius was born of a prominent family in the small Greek city of Megalopolis. He was befriended by Scipio the Younger and, as his secretary, accompanied his benefactor to the final destruction of Carthage in 146 B.C. during the Third Punic War. Later he witnessed the destruction and looting of Corinth, where he rescued priceless paintings from plundering soldiers. He once commanded a Roman expedition to explore the coasts of Africa.

The great growth in Roman power brought new sources of information about the world to the scholars of the day, and Polybius was one of the first to organize it and write about it. His works comprised forty-one volumes, of which the thirty-fourth was said to treat geography and its relation to history in terms not only of actual data, but also of their philosophical implications. It is a tragedy that we learn of this lost work only from later writers, or through incidental fragments included in other books.

Though Greece was conquered by Rome through the force of arms, the Greeks in reality made a cultural conquest of their Roman conquerors. Much of Roman art, literature, and science was based on Greek styles and information although, of course, the Romans provided many things worth study in their own terms. Then too, there were many important non-Roman scholars who lived and wrote within the Roman dominion.

It is not a completely accurate statement that says, "The Romans were too busy lawmaking and fighting for their overextended empire to give much attention to the arts and sciences and their literature." But there is an element of truth in it.

Although this period, by contrast with the former one, was somewhat lacking in geographical description and narrative, it nevertheless produced one of the great geographical writers of all times. His name was Strabo. Strabo's life-span of eighty-four years included the birth of Christ. His crowning effort was the compilation of a seventeen-volume work which he composed in Rome after extensive travels throughout the known world, beginning soon after his birth in

Asia Minor. A complete translation of Strabo's magnificent production, known simply as *Strabo's Geography*, is available today for the modern English-speaking reader. The first two of its volumes serve as an introduction; the next eight describe Europe. The eleventh volume is about remote Asia; the next three, about Asia Minor; the following one, about India and Persia. Book 16 tells of Assyria, Babylonia, Syria, and Arabia; the last book tells of Africa, principally Egypt.

In this one work, Strabo tried to show the interrelations between physical facts and human events. He admired Homer while seemingly despising Herodotus. Although his work was admittedly directed to statesmen and politicians, he did not treat Caesar's commentaries on the Gallic War as very important.

Another treatise of some interest is the geography by Pomponius Mela, written about A.D. 43. In guidebook fashion, this work offered all sorts of information about the lands bordering the Mediterranean Sea. A few years later, Gaius Plinius Secundus, often called Pliny the Elder, compiled an enormous thirty-seven-volume work, which he called *Historia Naturalis,* or *History of Nature.* Book 2 discusses systematic physical geography, including meteorology, and Books 3 and 4 discuss human geography. Unfortunately, these latter two volumes are uncritical and poorly organized.

In the next century, Dionysius Periegetes wrote his *Descriptive Account of the Habitable World,* which many centuries later was used in schools for teaching

27

both Greek and ancient geography. *Tacitus on Britain and Germany* is also a storehouse of information for that period.

The culmination of the classical period came with the mighty geographical efforts of Claudius Ptolemaeus, or Ptolemy. He knew more about the world than any of the geographers before him and, despite its errors and unknowing omissions, his map with its supplementary tables was to become a later standard for the civilized world.

Following Ptolemy's masterful compilations in the second century A.D., little in geographical writing and research—except imitations and abridgments of Ptolemy's work—followed for several centuries.

We turn our attention now to that long period extending roughly from the fall of Rome in the fifth century until the important activities of the fifteenth century. These thousand years have been called the Middle Ages. For Europe, the first half of this period is often regarded as the Dark Ages, because the stabilizing and civilizing influence of the Roman Empire had disintegrated, and because from those five centuries comparatively little of value in art, literature, science, or even architectural monuments has been inherited.

The Emperor Constantine had established Christianity as the official religion of the Roman Empire in the fourth century. This legacy became one of the principal foundations of medieval society. In the political vacuum caused by the dissolution of the empire, numerous petty princes and feudal overlords emerged with great local power in Europe, but with no real influence to bring unity and order over considerable areas. Religion alone—and of course the temporal power that was to be gained in its name—came to be the universal idea to which all else was subject. In these circumstances, original geographical research and writing did not flourish. The old or classical works were reinterpreted in theological terms. The Bible was regarded as the only infallible source of knowledge, and with regard to physical geography the Book of Genesis was considered the most important part. Anything in the earlier geographical literature that could not at that later date find biblical support was considered inconsequential, if not downright wrong. Paradoxically, however, even though the Church may have officially condemned all knowledge contrary to its purposes, the clergy of the time, especially the English and Irish, made it a practice to keep intact all the available works of the ancients. Thus, although official doctrine described the earth as flat, Macrobius and Capella, for example, kept alive the Ptolemaic idea of a spherical earth.

Many priest-scholars of the Dark Ages compiled encyclopedias. By the fifth century, the Spaniard Orosius had written his *Adversus Paganos Historiarum*, the first lengthy history from a Christian viewpoint. For many of its facts and for its style, his geographically oriented first chapter was based on Strabo, who also recognized a spherical earth. Virtually every encyclopedist for the next eight hundred years quoted Orosius.

Perhaps the most radically religious writer of all was Cosmas. His sixth-century *Topographia Christiana,* or *Christian Topography,* explicitly denies the possibility of anything but a flat earth. He found no support in the scriptures for any other shape; moreover, he regarded the suggested existence of antipodal creatures on a spherical earth as a defiance of logic. What would hold those upside-down creatures to such an earth?

The geography of the ninth century was essentially that of the fourth century. Maintenance of ideas rather than expansion of ideas was the watchword.

During the Dark Ages there was a certain amount of long-distance travel, much of it related to religious pilgrimages. From the travelers' reports little can be gleaned about the nature of people and places, although a fair knowledge about the routes and distances between sites of importance has been retrieved.

By the eighth and ninth centuries, it is true, a few writer-scholar-monks had begun to exhibit an intellectual curiosity about the earth's geography and to suggest that many hitherto unquestioned aspects of it should be examined anew. Included among these scholars were the English monk, the Venerable Bede, and the Irish cleric, Dicuil. It would be a mistake, however, to think that geography primarily occupied the attention of these gentlemen, and especially would it be an error to think that academic geography would soon be regarded as important.

It is true that the Crusades, beginning in the tenth century, occasioned travel, trade, and the interchange of ideas over vast areas, but the Crusaders were fighters, not scholars. Yet, all over Europe there were stirrings. Scholars were congregating in colleges such as those in Paris, Oxford, and Bologna.

Up until this time, an absence of Greek learning in its non-Latinized, non-Christian form had handicapped Western scholarship. The Arabs, on the other hand, had long used and improved on the Greek works. In Spain, particularly at places like Toledo, European Christians and Arab Moslems developed an exchange of ideas that was not possible before the Crusades. By the thirteenth century, Spain predominated in learning among European nations.

The introduction of Arabic studies to the Western world was of extraordinary importance. It brought to the West the important findings of ancient Greek science. With regard to geographers, it brought renewed interest in the earth's size, shape, and motions. The science and art of cartography began once more to receive attention. Knowledge concerning the earth and its motions, and concerning cartography, was something that could withstand the passage of the ages. The regional descriptions of writers like Herodotus and Strabo were judged no longer relevant, although they were considered valuable as historical pieces themselves, and as pictures of places in antiquity.

Of course, the world was not yet nearly ready to develop geography as a social science that might benefit from the subtle nuances of a scholar like Herodotus. Nor were the Europeans quick to assimilate the colorful and advanced regional and descriptive geography

31

of the Arab world which the Moslems themselves had produced.

Within a remarkably short time after the death of the prophet Mohammed in the seventh century, the Arab world had been transformed from a group of warring nomadic tribes to a flourishing civilization and culture.

By the latter part of the eighth century the city of Baghdad had become the Arab world's capital. On the crossroads of important overland and water transportation routes, Baghdad catered to merchants, scholars, and princes from many parts of the world. This circumstance, coupled with the intense desire of the Abbasid caliphs to foster intellectual and cultural development, led to a flourishing city.

Above all else, the Arabs were the pupils of the Greeks. Arab science is a continuation of Greek science, which it preserves, cultivates, and on a number of important points, develops and perfects.

Astronomy and geography, for special reasons, were of great importance to the Arabs. Precise establishment of directions was essential for religious reasons, because of the orientation of mosques toward Mecca. Further, the establishment of exact geographical coordinates through astronomical-geographical means was important to Arab astrology. Then, too, extremely long overland trips on holy pilgrimages or on commercial trading journeys required not only general geographical formulations for navigational purposes, but also special geographical knowledge of the availability of food, water, and shelter in a bleak and arid land.

Of importance to geographical thought was the

translation into Arabic of Greek geographical writings, which was included among the activities of a specially established and handsomely subsidized "Bureau of Translation." An organization for scholars engaged in original research was also established, and named the "House of Wisdom." To complement the Arab scholars, many Jews, Christians, and Hindus were employed.

The work of Ptolemy was translated, studied, and improved by groups of scholars. Especially important in this endeavor was al-Khwarizmi. He led sixty-nine scholars in writing the *Picture of the Earth*, essentially a description of a world map based on a Syrian copy of the Ptolemy map, but much improved in the areas of the Moslem world.

Ptolemy's astronomical statements showed up as the *Almagest*. Of course, Ptolemy viewed the earth as fixed in position, without motion. To preserve appearances, complicated orbits were assigned to all other heavenly bodies. This idea remained the ruling one until the sixteenth century.

The interests and activities of the Arab scholars were many and varied. One of the more important geographers was al-Idrisi, who worked for King Roger II of Sicily, making maps of the world. What he did is of importance, but his great interest to later scholars lies in the way he directed the investigations carried out by his staff in a carefully planned research program. Seventy-one maps were produced and, when placed together, formed a world map. His accompanying book, *Amusement for Him Who Desires to Travel Round the World*, contained many vivid regional descriptions.

33

Al-Balkhi also provided extensive regional descriptions and was followed by a long succession of students striving to improve on their predecessors' work. A final attempt to provide a great compendium of all the regional knowledge of Islam was essayed in the twelfth century by a freed Greek slave who took to himself the name al-Yaqut. His contribution has proved to be a most wonderful treasure of information concerning the age.

From the tenth century onward, Arab prowess declined, and Europeans stepped into power vacuums wherever they occurred. The Christian reconquest of central Spain in the eleventh and twelfth centuries opened the way especially for the acquisition of Arab learning. The intellectual side of Arab life made a deep impression on the conquerors. Latin translations of Arabic works on science were undertaken. People from different parts of Europe went to Spain in quest of knowledge. In Sicily, too, Arabic, Greek, and Latin were commonly used by cooperating scholars. Here was one important early impetus to the later European Renaissance. Over a Europe that had long been stifled by ecclesiastical dogmatism a revolutionary change began to sweep. Prejudices against the Moslems were sufficiently overcome to allow European acceptance and encouragement of Arab-Greek science. The translations into Latin of the vast literary geographic works —the regional descriptions of the Moslem world—were not accomplished, however, until after the great age of discovery.

As the various European nations extended their

range across the broad seas of the world, new facts about new places were heaped up by the reports of explorers and seamen. Navigation and cartography alternately led and followed the ever extending reaches of the European nations. Errors of observation and concept were gradually overcome as instruments were improved and theories developed. Commercial enterprise and military operations set problems to which the mathematics of the age provided answers in navigation and cartography. A systematic academic geography for its own sake was not yet regarded as a requirement of the age, however.

In the latter part of the sixteenth century, John Dee applied his mathematical abilities to the search for a northeastern passage to the Far East. His *British Complement of the Perfect Art of Navigation*, 1577, was written in hope of promoting England as the "Mistress of a Northern Empire."

Richard Hakluyt, the Elder, was a lawyer with a fondness for gathering economic and commercial information about trading possibilities in new areas. He served as an adviser to trading companies. The elder Hakluyt's cousin, Richard Hakluyt, the Younger, continued these endeavors. Although he did not travel extensively himself, his armchair research resulted in various publications extolling the virtues of British explorers and urging the nation to new overseas ventures. His light duties at Oxford University afforded him the opportunity to write *Divers Voyages to America* in 1582, *The Discourse of Western Planting* in 1584, and then, in 1589, *The Principall Navigations, Voiages,*

Traffiques, and Discoveries of the English Nation. This latter treatise was revised and enlarged several times as Hakluyt improved his descriptions and assembled new information.

Samuel Purchas was another geographer who had friends in court and maritime circles, and who joined those whose patriotism was combined with a profit motive and expressed itself through publications recounting the past glories of the nation and inciting it to more.

In this atmosphere of urgency about new facts and new opportunities, which existed both in England and on the continent of Europe, Varenius' call to a reconsideration of systematic principles was issued. Isaac Newton's selection and editing of Varenius' book to "assist the young gentlemen of Cambridge in perfecting their studies" was the factor that for a time shaped the course of academic geography both in British and American colleges.

In those British colonies that later became the United States, there were nine institutions of full college stature—Harvard (1639), William and Mary (1693), Yale (1701), University of Pennsylvania (1740), Princeton (1746), Columbia (1754), Brown (1764), Rutgers (1766), and Dartmouth (1769). At each of these colleges, geography was one of the half-dozen courses of study required by each student. It was generally offered by the Professor of Mathematics and Natural Philosophy. Along with astronomy, it was considered a branch of "mixed mathematics" and featured intensive studies of the terrestrial and celestial globes that were major elements in the "philosophical apparatus" of these colleges.

Newton's editions of Varenius were the most widely used textbooks for general geography, but there were additional texts by other British authors. Following the successful American Revolution, however, outcries against the continued use of British descriptions of American regions led to a replacement of these special geographies. The Reverend Jedidiah Morse wrote in the preface of his new *American Universal Geography* that "to depend on foreigners, partial to a proverb to their own country, for an account of the divisions, rivers, productions, manufactures, navigation, commerce, literature, improvements, etc., of the American states would certainly be a blot upon our literary and national character."

Jedidiah Morse himself undertook the preparation of American geographical texts to replace the British ones. *Geography Made Easy* (1784) was followed by the book mentioned above and by many others. Morse's books were enormously successful commercially, appealing as they did to the patriotic fervor of the new nation. He emphasized the superiority of America over the other countries of the world and provided the most comprehensive treatment of this nation to be found. Unfortunately, because of his uncritical acceptance of materials sent to him from many sources, his books were inaccurate and biased. Morse was not an original researcher, but rather a compiler, and a not too selective one, at that.

Although the intellectual challenge of Morse's books

was meager indeed, the fancy of the popular mind was caught. Geography became "popular," and Morse's books were found as often in the home as in the school. The term "geography" was becoming clearly and irreversibly associated with but one part of the subject, namely special (descriptive) geography.

In the colleges, geography disappeared from the curriculum during the first few decades of the nineteenth century. Courses emphasizing special geography, partly American, were now to be found in the elementary and secondary schools. There the subject was taught as one whose facts were to be memorized, and geography acquired the reputation of being "dry as dust." (Today it is still thought of in that way by many people, especially those who are not aware of the exciting developments that have recently taken place in geography and who do not know of the important positions geographers fill.)

Until just after the middle of the nineteenth century, geography generally remained in the situation described above. It was taught in the elementary and secondary schools, but not in the colleges, although the colleges did require that entrance examinations in the subject be passed.

In 1854, Arnold Guyot, a distinguished Swiss scholar, accepted the invitation of Princeton College to join its faculty as Professor of Geography. With this act, the subject was once more introduced into the colleges of the United States. Yale, Harvard, Pennsylvania, Columbia, and many other academic institutions followed Princeton's lead.

38

What was the philosophical base of this new excitement in academic geography? How had the subject become re-vitalized after its long dormancy?

Guyot viewed the earth teleologically—as the home divinely and especially created for man. Global in his outlook, he viewed geography as pertaining to all nature *and* human societies. Here now was general geography purposely aimed at interpreting and understanding human phenomena. A famous comment by Arnold Guyot has long been remembered. "To describe, without rising to the causes or descending to the consequences, is no more science than merely and simply to relate a fact of which one has been a witness." To Guyot and the other rising American geographers, a natural science of society was required—and was fortunately possible—to rival and balance the natural science of the physical world.

Although Guyot was Swiss, his geographical training had been German. In his day, German geography had advanced to high standing, principally through the efforts of two great men, Alexander von Humboldt and Karl Ritter. Although they did not collaborate in an official way, and were as unlike in scientific interest and research effort as they were in personality and disposition, these two men did engage in work that was naturally complementary.

Baron von Humboldt, an internationally known celebrity, not only was well read but also had traveled extensively. He was a scientific journeyer, observing detail and recording it systematically. He introduced and used new instruments. He was one of the first to use an improved chronometer in the attempt to determine longitudes more accurately, and to use a barometer for the determination of altitudes. Von Humboldt collected and studied many geological and botanical specimens, realized the value of guano deposits for fertilizer, studied volcanism, studied the appearances and institutions of various peoples of the world, and gathered documents on economic, political, and social conditions. After many journeys and the publication of many volumes, von Humboldt lived out his life as the scientific adviser to the King of Prussia.

Karl Ritter, who led a secluded academic life, was especially concerned with the problems of organizing geographic facts and concepts for educational purposes. In this connection he realized the value of the regional concept in geography. His interest in the study of non-human phenomena was secondary to his interest in man.

Both von Humboldt and Ritter died in 1859. Although working independently, together they had dominated and reformed academic geography in Germany. From this source came the ideas Guyot introduced to American college geography.

Eventually the teleological emphasis was changed, and evolution came to replace teleology as an organizing concept in human and physical geography. But continued emphasis on the physical environment as *determining* human activities prevailed, and many exaggerated statements were offered and excessive claims made for this point of view. Against these statements and claims many other scholars voiced objections, and in time younger geographers came to revolt —although the environmental determinists were not entirely wrong. Indeed, the physical environment always had and still does present limits to human activities. At low technological levels or in very rigorous physical environments, the limits of the natural environment come close to determinism. In more moderate environments and especially as physical science advances and the successful engineering based on it heaps up material benefits, the impact of man on man, and his combined social, economic, and political designs come also to shape the geographical patterns of human events.

After the passing of environmental determinism as academic geography's basic intellectual concept, nothing equally as challenging was offered immediately. Instead, regional geography—the description and evaluation of the various parts of the world—came to prevail. But, while "regions" represent an extremely important concept, it is one that is at the level of classification rather than at the level of predictive science. Hence, organized as regional geography, the subject as a whole was unable to continue to contribute importantly to a strong liberal arts curriculum. In the colleges where geography was important in colonial times and into which it was reintroduced in the middle of the nineteenth century, the subject is not now in prominence; its position was steadily weakened between the two world wars.

Since World War II, however, there have been remarkable developments. Currently in the United

41

States there are geographers who are making great progress in developing aspects of general geography, including not only systematic (physical), but also human geography. Mathematics is playing an important part here, also, and the idea of geography as a branch of mixed mathematics (today we would say "applied mathematics") is again strongly endorsed by some. The role that geography plays in the academic curriculum is undergoing some startling changes. The immediate future probably will witness a revolution in geographic instruction of a kind that occurs only once in a century.

3

Geography As a Science

Why should geography be included in any course of studies? Isn't geography just an elementary school subject? Is geography taught in college? Couldn't someone major in another subject in college and be just as well or better prepared to apply for the jobs that geographers hold? What do geographers do that is different from other jobs? These are some of the questions that were directed at the author and two of his colleagues during a recent lengthy conference of representatives from many fields of learning. It was the job of the three geographers to prepare a report presenting their view of their subject. Of course, any science is a growing, changing body of thought, and the geographers sometimes differed as to the exact nature of their calling, but in general they agreed on the following.

The essence of geography is the study of spatial relations. Through the centuries, geographers have described, classified, and predicted *locations*. It is their continuing concern for the eternal question *Where?* and their appreciation of its significance that has set geographers apart from their fellowmen. People in every society have always felt the importance of this question.

In geography, there are three levels that must be considered: description, classification, and prediction.

Many travel books and adventure stories are at the level of descriptive geography. Here, places are characterized according to their particular qualities; emphasis is on the uniqueness of places. No two places in the world, however small they may be, are exactly alike. Each has its own certain character and appeal, which can be equaled nowhere else.

To be sure, it is impossible fully to describe the unique, because the very terms of language themselves are general. A clever writer can convey the feeling of the uniqueness of a place by his skillful description of the particular way in which many things are there combined, however.

Descriptive geography depends largely on words and on general language. Besides the geographers, there are the historians, the novelists who emphasize local color, the journalists, the poets, and the essayists; often they all engage in geographic writing. Much of excitement and beauty has resulted from inspired description by those who know and love certain places. To the general public, such geographic writing, supplemented by attractive art work or colorful photographs, has an enduring appeal.

Sometimes, though, *description* of places alone is not sufficient to a particular task at hand; then *classification* of places might prove to be useful. It is at this level that geography develops its own methods, its own concepts, and its own critique.

Every square inch of the earth's surface differs in some way from every other square inch. To know everything about the whole surface of the world, or even a part of it, in inch-by-inch detail is of course impossible. Even if such knowledge were possible, classification in the geographic sense still would often be essential, and the detailed description of every possible place would not do instead. The very heart of geographical classification lies in that branch of the subject called regional geography.

Suppose we wanted to study the distribution of total annual precipitation (hail, mist, rain, sleet, and snow) for all the places on the earth. If we knew the amount at enough specific points, we could reliably estimate the precipitation at intervening points.

For purposes of planning any one activity such as a sales campaign, a military operation, or a study of natural vegetation, only certain ranges of precipitation might be thought critical. Thus, the whole area might well be divided into a few regions, each region having its appropriate limiting value of precipitation.

Temperature and, to a certain degree, surface elevations can, like precipitation, be figured fairly well for intermediate points from other known points. Other things—like languages spoken and styles of dress—cannot be estimated for intermediate places from information about other places, though certain other human phenomena can, as will be described later in the discussion of macrogeography.

In any event, whether the characteristics are natural or human, or whether intermediate points can be estimated or not, the regional method applies and is of importance.

Obviously there is no perfect set of natural regions, and what might be a valuable regional division for one purpose may be quite inadequate for another. The size and shape of each of the regions may be varied to suit a specific purpose.

Regionalization is much like classification generally. The classifier uses one set of terms to define all the members of a class, and recognizes that the differences among the members of that particular class are not as significant, for the purpose at hand, as are the differences of that class from all other classes. There is one element always present in regional classification, however; that element is *location*.

To determine useful regions for a given purpose, it is necessary to make operational categories from a virtually infinite variety of data, but the factor of location is always present.

When simple regions have been agreed on, whatever their purpose, each region may be considered as a set of particular places. Thus regions as sets of places respond to the operations that may be performed on sets as explained in set theory in mathematics. Therefore, multiple-factor regions and subregions are valid ideas similar to unions and intersects. Research is now progressing in this mathematical set theory-regional classification idea.

Of particular interest and importance here is the research being undertaken in expressing by maps the real phenomena of regions in the same manner as the graphical expressions in mathematical set theory, such as the circles and ellipses of Venn diagrams. Thus, geographers interested in the problems and methods of regionalization might regard the earth as representing, for them, the "set of all sets," with maps showing regional boundaries as representations of Venn diagrams as though literally drawn on the earth's surface.

It would be a mistake, however, to think that regional geography is nothing more than classification procedure and set theory, and that anyone well versed in just these two important topics can thereby be a good regional geographer, once he has learned how to handle properly the important geographic factor of location. The problems are more difficult than that. Intensive study and an ability that can be acquired only with considerable experience are required before proper decisions can be made as to what are the critical kinds of factors for any regionalization. Moreover, the regional method itself often reveals new functional relationships hitherto obscure but, once discovered, worth further systematic study.

But, as necessary as regionalization is, it is not the whole of geography. As in any science, so in geography, classification procedures such as regionalization stand between the level of simple description of individual details and the level of *prediction*.

In recent years, geographers have turned their attention to predictive geography. It deals with facts, as do all aspects of science, but it deals also with scientific theory—that which is a mixture of fact and logic.

Any geographic prediction of the location of phenomena on the earth—human, physical, or whatever—involves reference to *movements* such as circulation, diffusion, interaction, orbits, and flows. This is what distinguishes spatial, i. e., geographic, processes from other kinds of processes.

These movements, whether of rivers eroding the earth's mantle, or of the migration of people from rural to urban areas, produce changes in the spatial arrangement of features. Thus, spatial structures and spatial processes are ideas general enough to include a wide range of physical and human phenomena; the two ideas are always interrelated in a dynamic way in predictive geography.

One of the specific topics that modern research geographers have investigated with extraordinarily fine results is climatology, the science of climates. For example, the late C. W. Thornthwaite observed that, for a time, climatology threatened to become nothing more than the statistical averaging of individual meteorological elements by geographical areas. These elements were formerly regarded as temperature,

48

precipitation, atmospheric humidity, atmospheric pressure, and wind velocity. "But," said Thornthwaite, "the sum of the climatic elements that have been under observation does not equal climate. One element conspicuously missing from the list is evaporation." The combined evaporation from the soil surface and the transpiration from plants, together are called "evapotranspiration." Evapotranspiration is the movement of moisture from the earth to the atmosphere—the reverse of precipitation, which is the movement of water from the atmosphere to the earth.

Knowing precipitation alone does not tell us whether a climate is moist or dry. We must know whether precipitation is greater or less than the water needed for evaporation and transpiration. Moreover, we need to know how both precipitation and evapotranspiration rates vary throughout the year. Thornthwaite introduced the idea of "potential evapotranspiration"—the amount of water that would be evaporated and transpired from an area completely covered with vegetation if adequate moisture were always available. The potential evapotranspiration surface can be adequately estimated by using a mathematical formula with lists of temperatures and lengths of day. The map of this potential evapotranspiration surface is most important; when it is compared with measurements and estimates of actual evapotranspiration, an improved climate classification becomes possible. There have been many offshoots from this line of investigation, and many applications of it to practical problems (see page 74).

But to return to general considerations, geographical

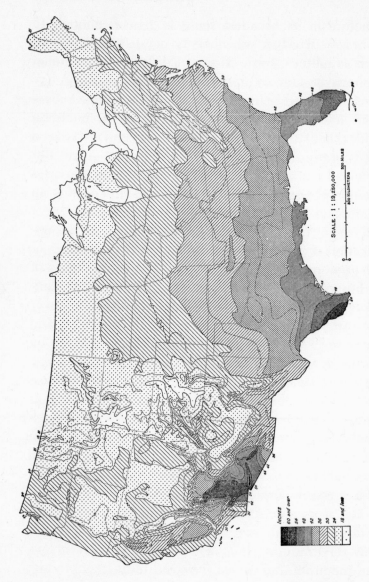

Map showing average annual potential evapotranspiration, United States.
(The Geographical Review, The American Geographical Society, N. Y.)

50

structure in its broadest sense is general enough to embrace all other subconcepts of spatial structure, such as pattern, form, distance, distribution, regional connectivity, and so on.

As suggested before, geographical form and movement are interrelated. Rain falling on a mountain erodes that surface. The mountain can be viewed as a fixed form down whose sides soil particles move. But ultimately a continued movement of soil particles changes the form of the mountain itself. There is an interaction between structure and movement.

The preceding paragraph is an example of the application of general ideas to a real physical surface of the earth and the movements on it. The same ideas of surfaces and movements can be used with other concepts also. Consider, for example, the distribution over the earth of atmospheric pressure. The great high and low pressure cells can be contoured like a surface by means of isobars, such as are seen on weather maps. Isobars are lines connecting those points on the surface that have equal barometric pressure. We can draw as many or as few of these as we wish by selecting a smaller or larger pressure interval to portray. If we draw enough such lines (i.e., if we select a small enough interval) we can get a very good representation of a pressure surface.

The steepness of gradients on this pressure surface determines wind velocities, even though air does not flow directly down such gradients. In any event, we can picture in our minds the wind ultimately eroding the high pressure surface and filling in the low. We cannot separate the dynamics of structure and movement.

The two examples cited above are drawn from physical geography. The same ideas of surfaces and movements can be applied equally well to man's sociological and economic activities.

At the American Geographical Society in New York there is under way a research program concerning the laws of geographical distribution over large areas, or the "macroscopic laws of geographical distribution." The American Geographical Society provides an ideal combination of research materials, encouragement, and inspirational direction for such a project. To date, the results of the research have been extremely promising.

Traditionally, in science, "macroscopic" refers to the *large* overall effects that result when all the single *small* (microscopic) units are joined together. As an example, the gas laws as first developed in physics in the seventeenth century by Boyle involve relations among temperature, pressure, volume, and the gas constant—characteristics of a gas which result from the *combined effects* of the molecules. The combined effects are predictable even though the behavior of no single molecule is. In fact, Boyle's great contribution was made in the absence of knowledge of the actual composition of the samples of gases he studied. It must be noted too that by making a detailed investigation and description of each of the molecules separately he would never have seen their larger, combined relationships.

In the same way, a series of small-area studies of the United States would never give a complete "geography of the United States." Only a large, macroscopic view will show the smaller elements in their true relationships.

In the current macroscopic research so far, it has been found that there exists a measurable factor of tremendous sociological importance, called "sociological intensity." It is much like its counterpart, temperature, in the physical world. It is not contained, nor is it measurable, in any one individual in a system, but is the result of the combined influence of all individuals. This influence necessarily varies from place to place. Proximity (nearness) of people to people is a principal ingredient of this sociological intensity. In this case, however, proximity is measured, not by the conventional population density (the average number of individuals in a given unit of space)—which has been found to be of less importance than previously thought —but it is measured by means of a factor known as "potential of population."

Potential of population measures the accessibility of a total population to a given place. Unlike *density* of population, which is purely local, the *potential* at a point includes a contribution from each person; the amount of his contribution is equal to the reciprocal of his distance from the point. The potential represents the entire population, and its value varies geographically. The value of total potential can be computed for as many points as required, and contours—called iso-potential lines—can be used to portray this surface, too.

A map of the potential-of-population surface for the United States was introduced earlier by Professor John Q. Stewart, Astronomical Physicist at Princeton University, in his attempt to help develop important concepts for social science. Later it was found that if the number of people and their distances apart were known, potential of population could be figured by the original gravitational equations of Isaac Newton and Joseph Lagrange—if number of people were substituted for mass, in the equations.

Just as temperature is a measure of molecular activity, so sociological intensity, or "social temperature," if you will, is a measure of sociological activity. The higher the intensity, the higher the rates at which money changes hands, first-class mail is interchanged, and telephone calls occur. The importance of poten-

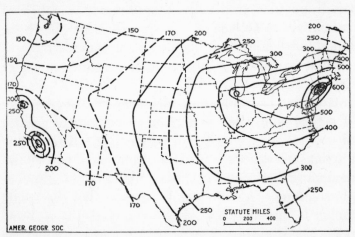

Map showing potential of population, United States, 1960, (thousands, persons per mile). Potential in shaded area is greater than 800,000 persons per mile. (The American Geographical Society, N. Y.)

tial of population as distinct from density of population also has been demonstrated with regard to the geographical variation in land values in the United States; average rents of dwelling units; urban taxes per capita; commodity prices; suicide rates; birth and death rates; city, county, and state areas; acreage of farms; areas of Federal Reserve districts; wholesale marketing district areas; road, railroad, and telephone wire densities; business failure rates; patents issued; the flow of bank checks; and the relative proportions of the various components of the total money supply. Spatial variations in all these things have a definite relationship to geographical variations in the potential of population.

At higher sociological intensities, the flow of information between people is more rapid, and a greater number of decisions must be made. These stress-inducing factors have been shown to have great bearing on problems of mental health and alcoholism.

Thus, it can be seen that human geography and the results of its research are of great importance to the broad general social sciences. Time, distance, number of people, and a few other dimensions are the basic categories upon which social theory might be built. Physical distance is just as important a dimension in the analysis of social phenomena as it is for physical phenomena. It is with this dimension that the geographer is basically concerned in his emphasis on location.

The geographer's major contribution to any integrated pattern of social science might consist of inves-

55

tigating the significance of distance—and its corollary, location—as a basic dimension of society. Emphasis in the research will not be on descriptive detail concerning the individual units of the system, but rather on the relations of the larger groupings in their spatial arrangements. Already the observable mathematical space-time-quantity regularities of society are being made explainable and the knowledge of geographical structure and process has been increased. Geographical phenomena taken as a whole are interconnected much more consistently and with a greater unity than are any of their individual parts. Geographic research that reveals these interconnections will do much to help unify all the social sciences as well as to further the development of physical science.

4

Applied Geography

Pure research in geography, as in any other subject, should be carried out without any regard for what its special and immediately useful applications might be. Unless researchers have complete freedom to follow new clues as they appear, and to allow the results of their research to be what they will, much of the valuable time and effort needed for a full development of their subject will be lost. Because researchers must often forgo additional exciting ventures in order to produce something immediately useful, they may lose some of the advantages they have already gained, and the same ground may have to be covered again and again by other investigators.

While it is true that pure research is best carried out

when there is no pressure for immediate practical applications of its results, it is also true that the most important applications often stem directly from pure research.

Among the basic ideas developed in unfettered geographical research is one that has been applied importantly to air flight.

As is well known, the least-distance path between any two points on a sphere, such as our earth, is an arc of a great circle. Stretch a string on the globe between New York City and Copenhagen, in Denmark, and if the string is tightly drawn, you will see that it also passes over northern Newfoundland and northern Scotland. This great-circle route starts off toward the northeast, but continually bends (ever so slightly) so that its final direction into Copenhagen is just south of east. This minimum-distance route is 3,840 statute miles or 3,339 nautical miles.

Any airline pilot wishing to fly from New York to Copenhagen so as to travel the least distance absolutely necessary would of course try to follow the above route exactly. Actually, nowadays, this route is almost never the one followed on any of the routine commercial flights between these two cities. Nor is this merely a peculiarity of the trips between these specific cities. The shortest-distance routes over broad oceans are rarely if ever followed.

This sounds uneconomical, doesn't it? It seems downright confusing when you learn further that overseas flight paths between two cities are rarely the same for two successive flights. Here is a case where pure geographic reasoning has been applied to an actual physical and economic problem, for a special purpose and with profitable results.

While it is true that the arc of a great circle represents the path of shortest distance between two points on the spherical earth, it is equally true that obstinately following a great-circle course on every flight would frequently lead to excessively long flight times, much passenger inconvenience, and added operating expenses.

When a long overwater flight is to be made through areas of varying wind direction and velocity, the attempt is now almost always made to select that path, however much longer in distance than the most direct route, which will require the minimum flight time. Deviations from the great-circle route can actually take the aircraft into areas where the prevailing winds may impede progress less, or even aid it, to an extent that more than offsets the effect of having to fly a greater distance; and the result is a shorter time en route than would have been required for the least-distance path. The objective is to find this path requiring least time en route. The collective mathematical and graphical flight procedures for this have become known as pressure-pattern navigation. The optimum flight path is of necessity shaped by the existing wind distribution, and hence, as will be shown, by atmospheric pressure patterns.

Only in the complete absence of wind in all regions at a given flight level could the most direct path—the shortest distance, or great-circle route—be safely assumed to be the optimum flight path. But on virtually no long-distance flight is the wind throughout the entire flight completely calm, nor is it of constant direction and velocity. Generally, from place to place over most of any flight there will be varied crosswind, headwind, and tail-wind components that drift the aircraft and sometimes impede, sometimes speed, it. Over large areas the wind direction and velocity may vary considerably. After many years of theoretical, mathematical, and empirical investigations, men have learned to put to most profitable use the particular physical environments in which they must navigate.

As has been mentioned earlier, we can describe and analyze atmospheric pressure distribution and wind flows in terms of surfaces and the movements on them. The wind, of course, does not flow down the simple pressure gradient, due to the earth's rotation. Rather, the wind flows down a so-called geostrophic gradient —a pressure gradient modified by the rotation of the earth.

Most readers are familiar with the daily weather maps in newspapers. These maps portray the variations in pressure reduced to some constant true altitude, generally sea level, and they provide an easily understood representation of the pressure system. On these maps the isolines connecting points of equal barometric pressure are called isobars.

On the maps actually used to plan minimum-time flights, the isolines are called contours (not to be confused with the contours on maps representing physical landforms). The lines drawn show the altitudes at which a constant pressure surface occurs. These lines indicate the true altitudinal variation of a constant pressure surface. Whether isobars or contours of this kind are used, the resulting maps are quite similar in appearance.

The simplified geostrophic-wind formula for navigation purposes is generally given as $W = 21.47 (D_2-D_1)/(X \sin L)$. W is the wind velocity in knots; (D_2-D_1) is the difference in feet in the true altitude of a constant pressure surface measured along the normal between two pressure contours (it is thus the contour interval); X is the distance in nautical miles along this normal between adjacent contours, and L is the latitude. The constant, 21.47, includes a number of conversion factors as well as the gravity constant divided by the earth's rotational speed. Wind direction parallels the contours. Appropriate substitutions in the formula can produce estimates of the tail-wind and crosswind components of the wind for an aircraft flying on any heading and at any true airspeed.

However, the full mathematical solution to the problem of determining the minimum-time path for any given type of aircraft through a wind field with varying wind directions and wind speeds is difficult. An endless procession of cyclonic lows and anticyclonic highs sweeps across an ocean like the North Atlantic, for example, in an ever changing series of relationships. This brings a continuous change in the least-time path from a given departure point to a specific destination, and that branch of mathematics called the calculus of variations is required to determine it, though suitable graphical approximations do exist.

It is not a new discovery that the fastest route between two places on the earth's surface is not necessarily the arc of a great circle. Marine navigators have long been familiar with the practicability in certain cases of widely separated tracks for voyages in opposite directions between the same two ports. Evidence exists to show that the first voyage of Columbus was made possible by his skillful utilization of the trade winds and the prevailing westerlies. And long before the Christian era, trading Arabs, conducting their commerce out of Africa with India, utilized the monsoons, with their seasonal wind shifts.

Although neither the ancient Arabs nor Columbus can be regarded as showing an early concern with a true optimum path, they did nonetheless indicate an interest in utilizing most effectively the physical environment in which navigation must be performed.

The first truly systematic approach to the problem of establishing precisely the unique least-time route for sailing ships between two ports can be found in the works of the American naval officer and physical geographer Matthew Fontaine Maury. From 1839 on, Maury extracted vast quantities of wind and current information from ships' logbooks, many of which had lain untouched for years. By collating these data with those from other sources, he was able to produce marine charts of winds and currents.

A principal feature of these charts was the wind roses showing variations in the wind velocities and the frequencies of directions. After assembling and analyzing enormous amounts of data, Maury was able to recommend least-time sailing routes that in many cases deviated greatly from the direct great-circle path. These least-time paths were selected after prodigious computation, and comparison of alternate routes, and were based on averages. Maury cautioned that only if his suggested routes were used consistently could their usefulness be seen in a considerable reduction of the average sailing times between ports.

Maury was so confident of the profit to be derived from the sustained use of his charts and sailing directions that he predicted an average saving of ten to fifteen days in the passage from New York to Rio de Janeiro. The subsequent fulfillment of this forecast aroused great interest in these charts and sailing directions on the part of mariners of all nations, and Maury was able to secure their cooperation in recording winds and currents in various regions. At an international convention in Brussels in 1853, Maury's system of uniform recording and reporting of oceanographic data was adopted for naval vessels and merchant fleets for virtually the whole world. Continued improvement in the sailing directions was thus made possible, and the seasonal shifts in the least-time paths were more fully exploited.

The eminent British anthropologist, Sir Francis Galton, is remembered principally for his work in eugenics, heredity, and the study of genius, and for his method of identification by fingerprints. But, in addition, his contributions to geography, navigation, and

63

meteorology were many, varied, and important, and ranged from a discussion of the art of travel to a memorandum on the construction of isochronic charts, with lines for comparing times along any two routes between a departure point and a point of destination —and describing the progress of a sailing vessel through a field of varying winds.

Galton's memorandum concerning sailing vessels was used by Giblett in 1924 as the basis for finding the minimum-time path for airships. Unlike sailing-ship methods, which had been based on average conditions, Giblett's method was designed to be used with currently existing winds, and included the combined influence of wind and propeller in establishing the optimum path. The graphical methods most widely used at present for the commercial airlines' transatlantic route-planning are direct descendants of the Giblett formulation.

The slow speed of airships, coupled with their long endurance in the air without refueling, made their flight planning particularly suitable for optimum-route considerations. Dr. Hugo Eckener, the brilliant German aeronautical engineer who designed and flew many airships, was a keen student of weather before he ever began to fly. His success in piloting the ZR-3 (later the "Los Angeles") on a transatlantic airship crossing in 1924, and then commanding the "Graf Zeppelin" on its global flight in 1929 was in part due to his remarkable ability to use the changing pressure systems to the greatest possible advantage. His many subsequent Atlantic crossings could never have been accomplished had he attempted to maintain the great-circle course westbound, in direct opposition to the prevailing westerlies. In fact, head-wind components of 50 knots (and these are commonplace) would have held his airship stationary, and wind velocities in excess of this would have caused any airship headed directly into the wind to fly backward.

In utilizing the most favorable winds, Eckener zigzagged all over the ocean, often making up for the lack of widespread and reliable forecasts for winds aloft by flying at low altitudes for which reliable steamship observations could be obtained and had meaning.

The extreme importance to airship navigation of adjusting to pressure patterns was shown in the joint report in 1929 of the British Meteorological Office and the Airship Flying Staff of the Royal Air Force. Wind conditions were estimated from the long series of daily synoptic charts of the North Atlantic, prepared jointly by the Deutsche Seewarte of Hamburg, and the Danish Meteorological Institute. Allowances were made for changing weather en route. It was ascertained that flight times could vary by as much as two to one between the best alternative and the great-circle route. That is to say, of two airships departing simultaneously from Cardington, one might reach Lakehurst in only two and one-half days by taking maximum advantage of winds, whereas the other, following the great-circle route, might take five days.

The 1930's were marked not only by increased theoretical and mathematical interest in optimum flight paths, but also by rudimentary attempts of the early commercial airlines to adjust the routes and schedules of their 110-knot aircraft to use most efficiently the changing physical environment confronting them. For example, on the San Francisco-Honolulu flight it was often necessary to route the flight via Los Angeles for refueling, then southwestward into the region of sub-tropical high pressure, before turning westward to Honolulu. This was done to avoid the deep lows that frequently centered on the direct route.

In the North American-European service it was possible in the summer to fly the North Atlantic both ways, with a stop in Newfoundland in each direction, and with a reasonable pay load, if the flight was adjusted to pressure systems. In the winter, however, the return flight from Europe was often routed down the African coast, across the South Atlantic to South America, and through the West Indies to New York, with refueling stops along the way. Such routes were adopted, not in search of a true least-time path, but just to make the return trip possible at all.

Two apparently unrelated and unexpected developments were ultimately combined to great advantage. World War II necessitated many long overwater flights for the ferrying of aircraft themselves as well as of military personnel and supplies. Navigators in the Air Transport Command operating over great-circle routes generally divided their flights into zones of equal width, for each of which a required wind-drift correction to keep the aircraft on course was computed. But in actual flight some of these navigators applied only the average of the individual zone drift corrections in a single correction, so that one true heading was flown throughout the entire flight (save for late corrections to compensate for forecast errors). Of course, the aircraft in flight were often blown far off the great-circle course to one side or the other. Invariably, however, they came into destination with only minor late corrections to the heading. In a sense, the navigators followed the aircraft's course by constant position-fixing, taking over the direction only near the end of the flight.

It was not surprising that one average drift correction worked so well, but what was astonishing about these flights was the great saving in time (and fuel) that frequently resulted. Beating flight-plan time by as much as two hours on a scheduled twelve-hour flight was not uncommon. Although on rare occasions these single-heading flights did take slightly longer than the great-circle flight-plan time, they so frequently beat the flight plans by comfortable margins that it became obvious that something systematic was at work.

About this time the radar altimeter was developed. Now, at last, navigators had a device for measuring absolute altitudes above the ocean, to complement the long-used pressure altimeter by which they had obtained distances from pressure-level differences. By simultaneous measurement of absolute altitude and pressure altitude, navigators were now able to determine certain characteristics of the pressure systems through which they flew (and could also obtain "pressure lines of position" as a navigation aid to add to their stock of lines of position obtained by celestial, radio, radar, loran, and visual aids).

Utilizing data associated with both these developments, a system of single-heading navigation was developed, utilizing only the geostrophic-wind formula, and requiring as data only the absolute altitude at departure and destination and the constant-pressure altitude at which the flight was to occur.

Used consistently, this system of navigation afforded considerable saving despite the occasional unduly long flight. In addition, the striking simplicity of the system had a strong appeal to practicing navigators. But alas, it was too good to be true. Further investigation revealed why the single-heading flights, under certain conditions, did lead to longer flight times than those along the great-circle path. Such circumstances include the case in which the great-circle route passes through a region of light, variable winds between two low-pressure cells. In this instance, the single-heading track across would at first diverge to the right of the great circle, whereas the true minimum-time path would at first diverge to the left and then converge toward destination. A number of corrective measures that partly solved the difficulties were proposed, but they were, in general, burdened by awkward procedures and laborious computations.

It became clear that a method other than single-heading flight was required. Attention was given to developing a quick graphic method for operational purposes that would permit direct determination of the desired path to the desired destination alone and that could be easily modified to accommodate the ever increasing regulations for in-flight air-traffic control.

Shortly thereafter, such a modification to the Giblett time-front method was proposed as makes everyday close-planning approximations of the true minimum-time path possible when this path is constrained to two dimensions, and the pressure distribution is regarded as unchanging during the time of the flight.

Now, although an excellent operational graphical solution to the optimum-flight problem exists, theoretical and observational investigations continue, and high-speed electronic-computer solutions and "four-dimensional," or 4-D, flight-planning research—including changes in atmospheric pressure through time—are likely to lead to important results.

Although this brief history ignores some of the major contributors and their work, it does convey some sense of the chain of events and ideas that has led to the present route-selection and navigation practices based on the application of geographic ideas, and serves to show how these have helped to make modern commercial airline operations across the oceans reliable, fast, comfortable, and safe.

Heretofore, we have defined optimum-flight-path planning in terms of expected time en route. But optimum operations in the broadest sense include much more than this. For safe as well as economically efficient flight, due regard must also be given to weather elements other than wind and pressure. Fog, icing, and turbulence cannot be ignored.

The track requiring the least fuel is not always the least-time track. Engine performance must be considered with respect to altitudes, temperatures, and methods of cruise—whether, for example, maximum range must be achieved at the price of faster speeds. The lack of emergency airfields may prevent safe operation over certain routes. The nature and location of ground aids to navigation, such as radio stations, weather ships, and loran stations, exert an influence as well.

Since flight planning is not done completely in accordance with known facts, but rests in part on predictions, such things as faulty meteorological forecasts and navigational errors can cut deeply into the efficiency of an operation. Happily, present-day forecasting is excellent, and flight navigators have attained a remarkable level of competence. By judicious use of the pressure and absolute altimeters, many flight navigators are able to detect pressure-system changes while in flight. By using the "pressure profile" technique coupled with current data radioed from other sources, they can redraw their weather maps in flight, replan the remainder of the flight and, if radio clearance can be obtained from an air-traffic control center, put the new plan into immediate effect. Clearance to change flight plan while en route is not always forthcoming, however; in fact, the original flight plan itself will certainly have in it a number of compromises necessary to meet traffic control requirements.

The airspace over the North Atlantic is becoming an increasingly valuable resource. Regulations state that each aircraft must be separated from all others by at least one of the following: (1) a lateral separation of 120 nautical miles; (2) a vertical separation of 2,000 feet; (3) a longitudinal separation of 30 minutes of flying time. Because of the air traffic constantly going into and coming out of the great number of airports, further complications result. Additional restraints are added by the necessity to depart from, or arrive in, America or Europe by flying only over certain prescribed control points, such as Goose Bay, Gander, and Torbay, in Newfoundland, or Nantucket, Massachusetts, in the United States, and Sumburgh, Prestwick, and Stornoway, in Europe.

Furthermore, local airport traffic restrictions must be observed, military requirements occasionally make heavy demands on the airspace, and sometimes large areas or certain altitudes are blocked to commercial use. Another condition is that the flight track of commercial aircraft must cross every multiple of 10° of longitude at a whole degree of latitude.

Because flights must meet all the limitations here set forth, and other important ones not mentioned, they can never fly least-time routes exactly as desired. Modifications must always be made. The ideal minimum route is virtually always considered first in present-day operations, however, and the flight plan that is filed with air traffic control adheres to it as closely as regulations permit.

Air traffic control would be far simpler if certain established routes were *always* followed. As we know, this is not the case. The constant search for the optimum route through the ever-changing pressure patterns means that for all practical purposes the same route is never flown twice.

As aircraft speeds increase, the optimum flight paths at a given pressure level tend to come closer to the great-circle route. Therefore one might argue that the amazingly shorter flight times of the jets over the flight times of piston aircraft would render needless the concern over flexible tracks, which might save only a few minutes. But even a few minutes saved are valuable in jet operations. Remember, too, jets operate at higher altitudes than piston aircraft, and in general encounter winds of higher velocities.

Despite the future's promise of ultrasupersonic passenger rockets operating in the troposphere or mesosphere, the immediate problems of improving, planning, and putting into use the optimum flight paths loom ever more important in the always quickening pace of international air travel, with the attendant rise in difficulties of air traffic control. Owing to lack of information, there has been difficulty in formulating an opinion on the increasing traffic-control problems. Informal discussions with controllers suggest that the areas of greatest congestion lie between Gander, Newfoundland, and Shannon, Ireland. Unfortunately, the data on origins, destinations, frequencies, and routes have never been properly assembled for analysis.

Maps showing areas of aircraft density, with altitude and track conflict plotted geographically by aircraft type and route and with appropriate meteorological data, would be extremely desirable. Attention should be given to the whole problem of seasonal variation. Although the completely flexible track for each flight is definitely preferable to *one* fixed track, the possibility of seasonally fixed tracks adjusted as well as possible to the various departure points and destinations in Europe and North America should be investigated. The gain to traffic control and ease in locating navigational facilities might well offset the loss due to fixed-track navigation. Whatever the final solution may be, it is obvious that it must represent a compromise between completely flexible tracks and completely rigid routing. A great deal of work needs to be and can be done in this matter. Further applications of the results of research in pure geography to the demands of the air-traffic control problem are needed.

Another important example of applied geography concerns the use of the potential-evapotranspiration concepts developed by Thornthwaite and his associates. While this research was at first done independently, without regard to possible economic implications and applications, the results have been extremely useful in this connection.

Potential evapotranspiration is defined as the amount of water that would be lost by evaporation and transpiration in a given time period from a surface completely covered with vegetation, if there were sufficient water in the soil at all times to be used by that vegetation. Maps showing the geographical variation in potential evapotranspiration were developed,

73

based on a mathematical equation using only temperatures and length of daylight from place to place and time to time. The factor, potential evapotranspiration, and its allied concepts provided an important basic step toward a classification of climate and climatic-geographic regions.

The possibility (and the future realization) of the useful applications of these concepts to economic problems came when it was discovered that potential evapotranspiration is also a direct measure of the rate of plant development. If, in a given time period, a certain potential evapotranspiration occurs, then a plant will progress toward maturity by a certain amount. Independent of its time and place of growth, each type of plant requires its own certain number of potential-evapotranspiration units in order to pass through each of the stages from germination to maturity.

But specific places and specific time periods vary in their rate of output of potential-evapotranspiration units. For example, along the eastern seaboard in the United States, development occurs slowly in winter, if at all; reaches a maximum rate in summer; slows down in autumn; and is again at a minimum during the winter. Of course, the rates at all seasons are greatest in southern Florida and least in northern Maine. The total annual accumulation near Miami, Florida, amounts to over twice that of Van Buren, Maine. Thornthwaite's map for the whole of the United States clearly shows the variation for the entire country as a contoured surface.

Leslie Curry, especially, has described the significance of this map in economic terms and has showed the necessity of understanding the interrelatedness of "economic time" and "economic space" in planning the commercial activities of agriculture, and other programs directly or indirectly related to agriculture.

For example, based on these concepts, farm labor and equipment can be more profitably used throughout the year by proper scheduling of planting and harvesting to take maximum advantage of seasonal changes in prices of agricultural commodities. Again, improvement in the timing of farming practices over wide areas of the United States has helped somewhat to better the unfortunate conditions of many migrant workers who often have had long periods of enforced idleness.

Planning for the geographical location and seasonal use of warehouses and other storage and transportation facilities for many important agricultural commodities has also been carried out.

Not only are these ideas which have been developed in pure research enormously important to agriculture and its service industries, but they also aid us greatly in other activities. Particularly is this seen in the fuel oil, gas, or other heating activities. These industries, of course, find their operations of purchase, storage, delivery, and maintenance closely linked to climatic conditions. Although here, as with agriculture, the vagaries of the weather introduce planning difficulties, timing acitvities can be scheduled within reasonable limits. Geographic and temporal variations

75

in our climatic environment require the insights and techniques of geographers in the attempt to understand them. Climate is still a basic timing mechanism in many aspects of modern life. A variety of scientists, from historians studying the manorial system of farming to anthropologists interested in the social calendar of a primitive people, have applied geographical analysis in many ways. Even at the level of national policy for agriculture, this geographical research cannot safely be ignored.

A final example of useful applications of geographers' efforts is taken from another country. It is only one from a great many that could have been chosen. The emphasis in this case is upon classification, and the results of the work have become not only national but international in their scope.

In the spring of 1926, Dr. L. Dudley Stamp resigned from the Professorship of Geography and Geology in the University of Rangoon, Burma, to return to his native England to become the Sir Ernest Cassel Reader in Economic Geography at the London School of Economics.

This turn of events led to a special emphasis by Dr. Stamp on a long-standing interest of his—the detailed geography of Britain. As he studied this subject with growing intensity, he became aware of what he considered serious gaps in the knowledge.

Although nearly every candidate for a degree in geography in British universities at that time had, at some stage of his training, prepared a report on a variety of details of some small area of Britain, only a small part of the country had been covered. More-over, because a wide variety of viewpoints and methods had been employed, little readily comparable data had been produced.

Then, to quote Dr. Stamp, "the idea began to crystallize in my mind of organizing a field-to-field survey of the whole country, covering every acre and recording its use, and then of preparing a report or description of the work. Two main matters had to be settled —the information to be collected, and the organization to be developed in collecting it.

"With regard to the information to be collected, it was essential to draw up a scheme applicable to the whole country, so that direct comparison between one area and another would be possible; it was essential to have the scheme simple enough to be understood by voluntary workers with varied or little training."

A plan was formulated early in 1930 and tested during the summer by Dr. Stamp and a few of his students. A simple, workable scheme was developed. Modest financial support was secured and a staff maintained. Both budget and staff were later greatly augmented. (Dr. Stamp noted that many of the applicants for the positions had ruled themselves out by declaring themselves fearful of the ambitious nature of the project!)

British Ordnance Survey base maps on various scales were obtained. Cooperation from educational authorities made it possible for the actual fieldwork to be carried out by children in the British schools. They did a magnificent job in recording forests, mead-

77

ows, arable lands, moors, heaths, orchards, wasteland, and so on. The completed Land Utilization Survey stands as a monument to them. Virtually all the land of Britain had been observed and its land use recorded before the beginning of World War II in 1939. Some 10,000 schools and 250,000 children took part, supervised by their teachers.

The benefits to Britain later were enormous. Educators also were enthusiastic about the immediate benefits to the schoolchildren. Especially noted were: (1) training in careful map reading; (2) accuracy of observation, with the knowledge that others would use and judge the observation; (3) completeness of observation; (4) the arousing of interest in the why and wherefore of what is found to exist; and (5) the awakening of civic consciousness and the idea of social service. The teachers and the children in the more remote areas were made to feel that they were doing something that brought them into direct contact with the life of the whole country and that the work could not have been complete without their little bit.

The Land Utilization Survey produced a remarkably detailed and accurate inventory of land use in Britain. In wartime Britain, when land as well as other resources was in desperately short supply to meet all the demands upon it, many decisions vital to the nation's very survival found their basis in facts provided by the survey.

Land use changes through time, and thus new surveys are necessary. To augment the work of the earlier survey, to keep it current, and to enlarge the applications, a Ministry of Town and Country Planning operating at the level of high policy was established by the British government in 1943. Many geographers now work closely with this ministry.

At a Congress of the International Geographical Union in Lisbon, Portugal, in 1949, a project was organized to establish a World Land Use Survey. The idea was supported by the United Nations Educational, Scientific, and Cultural Organization (UNESCO). Progress has been slow but measurable. Many unresolved problems such as organization, financial backing, operating methods, and classification standards remain. But enthusiasm continues high. In Canada, Tanganyika, Nyasaland, Cyprus, Puerto Rico, Malta, Lebanon, Union of South Africa, Azores, France, Switzerland, Nigeria, Iraq, West Germany, Italy, Burma, Ceylon, India, and the United States some work has been done in a manner that allows integration of the results into the tentatively agreed-on world classification. No country, however, has taken up the work with greater zeal than Japan, where the existing intensity of land use is already high and careful planning for the future has a high priority.

The Land Utilization Survey of Britain in the 1930's has often been likened to the Domesday Book survey in the Middle Ages, but that survey had an ulterior motive: taxation. The modern inventory had none; its object was simply to record the facts.

Just as in all other branches of science, the "pure researcher" in geography considers himself concerned only with the search for new knowledge; he is content

—in fact, he prefers—to leave to others such practical applications as can be made of his findings. People in general need to realize that the most useful applications of research come, in the long run, not from work done to solve immediate problems, but rather from the work of those whose interest is at the theoretical level. Here both classification and functional relationships must be understood, and both regional and predictive geography are important.

5

Globes and Maps

Geographers make and use globes and maps.

Distinguished men and women also seem to like having them at hand when they pose for photographic portraits. Globes, handsomely colored and carefully delineated, are most attractive when cradled by highly polished and obviously expensive wood. Such globes are indicators of the affluence and prestige of their owners and attest to these persons' world view.

Globes can be status symbols. They have about them a wonderful air of solid respectability and erudition. Decorators, too, delight in them. Their mountings and markings can be varied so that their spherical simplicity can be made to enhance the appointments

81

of any room, whether it be Early American or modern Swedish.

Maps, too, are like this. Some of them very decidedly can be appreciated for their aesthetic qualities and can be included to great advantage in certain decorative schemes.

But maps and globes properly conceived and carefully executed are, as geographers insist, something else, too. They are scientific instruments. They are models of the world on which we live—selective models, it is true, yet models nonetheless. Consequently, from a study of them one can learn a great deal of importance and interest. They are as necessary to some of man's most profound and significant undertakings as to his daily routines. Proper uses of them reveal relationships of excitingly high intellectual content. Some exercises and games performed with globes and maps can be wonderfully diverting as well.

Before any really good scientific model can be made, a great deal of knowledge must be accumulated about the thing the model is to represent. The gathering of knowledge about the earth is the concern of geographers.

Let us think of the size and shape of the earth, and a miniature model to represent it, first stating some of the important things we now know about these aspects of the earth. After that we can look at the particular difficulties and the methods employed in overcoming them when we attempt to make a model.

It must always be remembered that sound knowledge about these matters was not piled up irrevocably through the ages. What was once learned was again forgotten in some cases, and had to be discovered once more, at the expense of great time and effort.

The problems of the shape and size of the earth are physical problems, and the observations made and the evidence gathered about them are best analyzed, and the conclusions reached are best stated, in mathematical terms. While the knowledge arrived at by geographers and astronomers through the ages was stated and was to be understood only in these terms, there have always been many presumably well-educated persons who have lacked the scientific background that would allow them to appreciate the strength and pertinency of mathematical arguments.

At a lower level are the masses in the world, uneducated throughout most of past history and still so in some parts of the earth. They do not admit the possibility of proof by reason about anything that lies beyond immediate contact through their own senses. But this is only a relative thing—for the best-educated and most brilliant of all men, too, have their images and sentiments standing between them and reality. Scientific statements are never final and are always subject to improvement as man comes closer and closer to purely objective thinking. Science will always be ahead of most of us, and its full implications will escape us, for we judge the world and the activities in it—human as well as physical—in terms of the way we think they ought to be.

The earth is a perfect sphere—that is an extremely fine approximation of its true shape. But, if we insist on a statement that is at once simple and yet *absolutely* accurate, we find that we cannot make one—for the earth is not equivalent to any regular figure. Simple refinements to the statement that the earth is a perfect sphere can be made to accommodate actual measurements of the earth's shape, however, and still allow us to regard the earth as having a regular figure.

If we measure the earth's diameter between two opposite points on the Equator, we find it is roughly 25 miles longer than a diameter taken from the North Pole to the South Pole. We can then consider the outline of the earth to be an ellipse with a major and a minor diameter at right angles to each other, and the face of the earth to be the surface of rotation of this ellipse. This regular figure is an oblate spheroid; the earth as an ellipsoid thus departs from true sphericity in that it bulges somewhat at the Equator and is flattened in the vicinity of the poles.

Since we have not as yet said what the lengths of the two diameters are, however, you do not know whether the 25-mile difference represents a large amount or a small one. Moreover, big and small differences are terms that are conditioned somewhat by the particular use to which the information is to be put: that is to say, whether we need the information to facilitate the launching of a rocket to Venus or merely to plan a lengthy world cruise that takes advantage of the most pleasant weather in the Northern and Southern hemispheres at a not too exorbitant cost.

The actual sizes of the earth measurements will be given when the earth's magnitude is discussed below, but for the time being let us continue just to consider the problem of describing the earth's true shape.

The surface of one particular oblate spheroid is a closer approximation to the true shape of the earth than is that of a sphere. But an oblate spheroid—or, as it is sometimes called, an ellipsoid of rotation—is only approximately the shape of the earth. Actually, the earth's surface is not smooth. It has elevated areas and depressions whose variations from perfect smoothness are quite complex. This irregular pattern of variation is called surface relief.

Newton's classical theory of gravitation provided the intellectual basis for expecting that accurate measurements made in the eighteenth century would show the earth to be somewhat like an oblate spheroid, and indeed they did. But only if the earth were entirely covered by water that was free of the slightest ripples might its true shape coincide with that of an oblate spheroid. Actually, land can be found higher and lower than this water surface.

Many, many thousands of globes are in use today in homes, offices, classrooms, and other places. The manufacturers of these globes all tried to make them perfectly round. (In addition, there are certain special "globes" made purposely not round, like the Dymaxion globe with its fourteen flat faces of squares and triangles.) Of course, no globe has ever yet been made that is *absolutely perfectly* round, but that is the idea that is being imitated. The question now is, How nearly does a spherical model like a home or classroom globe represent the shape of the earth?

85

To answer this question, some of the earth's actual measurements must be introduced. By one series of measurements, the polar diameter of the earth has been found to be about 7,902.634 miles, and the equatorial diameter, about 7,926.817 miles. The ratio of the difference between these two diameters and the equatorial diameter gives approximately 1 in 300 parts: that is, merely about one-third of one per cent. If you have a globe in your home with *exactly* a ten-inch equatorial diameter, the polar diameter would have to be 9.96949+ inches to represent correctly to scale the polar flattening of the oblate spheroid depicting the earth. Actually, not even the sharpest eyes could detect the difference in these two lengths.

But in order to show accurately the surface relief —the mountains and valleys—and the ocean bottoms, shouldn't the face of our model globe be rougher in some spots than in others?

The world's highest peak, rising 29,028 feet above sea level, is Mount Everest in the Himalaya, and the greatest ocean depth yet sounded is in the Pacific Ocean just east of the Mariana Islands. The depth there is approximately 37,800 feet. These two departures from mean sea level represent about .07 of one per cent and .09 of one per cent, respectively, of the equatorial diameter of the earth. Needless to say, this circumstance, too, could not be detected by eye if it were *possible* somehow to represent it to scale by some extremely precise manufacturing process that globemakers do not have.

In 1959, calculations derived from the data of the

Vanguard I satellite orbit revealed further that the North Pole is 50 feet higher than formerly assumed and the South Pole is 50 feet lower. In the northern middle latitudes the earth's surface averages 25 feet lower than previously believed, and averages 25 feet higher in the Southern Hemisphere's middle latitudes. These differences are infinitesimally small when represented on a ten-inch globe.

Our conclusion is that we make only an extremely small and virtually undetectable mistake by trying to make perfectly spherical globes. If you were a giant who could hold the earth in his hands as you might now, at your actual size, hold a billiard ball, you would find it equally smooth. In fact, if the billiard ball were a cue ball that had been used often, it might seem the rougher of the two.

The size and shape of the earth are only two of its important aspects; the earth's motions need to be studied, also. The earth rotates daily on its inclined axis and revolves annually through the seasons on its orbit about the sun. Then, too, there is the matter of the precession of the equinoxes, but as Rudyard Kipling would say, "That's another story."

Now that we know something about the earth's shape and size, we can make decisions about the shape and size of our model of the earth—a globe. For example, suppose you decided on a sphere that had a twelve-inch diameter. What is the linear scale of such a representation of the earth?

The circumference of the earth can, for illustrative purposes, be regarded as about 25,000 miles. The circumference of our model with the twelve-inch diameter is about 37.7 inches. In 25,000 miles there are 1,584,000,000 inches, so that the ratio of 37.7 inches to 1,584,000,000 inches yields the statement that the linear scale of our globe is about 1: 42,000,000. That is to say, for example, that a line six inches long on the globe represents a line about 252,000,000 inches, or nearly 4,000 miles, long on the earth, and a length of one inch on the globe depicts a length of approximately 666 miles on the earth.

After the decisions of shape and scale have been made, we can decide what features of the earth's surface to represent. On the vast majority of globes ever made representing the earth, the oceans and landmasses have been differentiated, although the accuracy with which this has been done has, of course, increased as explorers gradually have come to visit all parts of the earth's surface and have gained knowledge of them.

Many other things—such as landforms, cities, political boundaries, ocean currents, and quite too many items ever to enumerate successfully here—have been shown with varying accuracy on globes. Take the latitude and longitude lines now almost invariably shown: a long story lies behind the establishment of this system of coordinates of location on the earth's surface—a story too long to tell here, but one that the interested can find in other books.

About 150 B.C., Crates, a Greek, made a terrestrial globe with a ten-foot diameter, one of the earliest ever made. He showed the earth as divided into four habitable but separate regions, each surrounded by water. His known world—including adjacent but small parts of Europe, Africa, and Asia—constituted one of these quarters. He conjectured about three other habitable parts, and in a sense anticipated discoveries that were not made until sixteen centuries later in North and South America and Australia.

The Egyptian geographer, Ptolemy, outlined specifications and provided extensive tables of data for making globes and globe maps in the second century A.D.

Although the Arabs kept geographical learning alive during the Dark Ages in Europe, it was not until the thirteenth century that Europeans began to be interested in globes. For over a thousand years, Christian Europeans held the earth to be flat, with Jerusalem at its center. Scholars in the thirteenth century revived Aristotle's arguments favoring sphericity, and this led to a revival of Ptolemy's works. This new awakening of interest probably was related to the improvement of sailing vessels, which now made long voyages possible.

One of the most famous globes ever made was that by Martin Behaim in 1492. It still exists today and is the oldest known globe extant. Christopher Columbus is believed to have seen it, and his study of it is said to have made him more determined than ever to gain financial support for an attempt to sail westward to the Orient.

Of course, Columbus did sail on his planned voyage, and discovered America in 1492. That he believed he had reached the Far East and did not realize he had discovered new land is very likely a true story, for the Behaim globe showed only scattered small islands westward from Europe to Asia. In fact, it showed the world's circumference too small by about one-quarter in terms of what Behaim believed the scale of his globe to be. If Columbus had really known the much greater *real* distance from Europe westward to the East Indies, he might very well not have sailed at all.

Behaim had made his globe for his townspeople in Nuremberg, Germany. It was elaborately colored. The seas were dark blue, and the land areas were brown, with patches of green to represent forests, and silver to show ice. Pertinent flags and coats of arms were drawn inside political boundaries. Some purely artistic devices were also used for decorations. In addition, among the welter on his globe, Behaim included some eleven hundred place-names.

Replicas of the Behaim globe may be seen in several museums and societies—including the American Geographical Society of New York City—and recently a commercial map and globe company has made miniatures of the Behaim globe.

The first globe that showed the Americas as large continents was produced in 1523 by Johannes Schöner, also a native of Nuremberg.

Many men distinguished by their accomplishments in other fields were also interested in globe-making. The many-sided Renaissance genius, Leonardo da Vinci, designed a set of globe maps. The famous Danish nobleman and astronomer, Tycho Brahe, made a six-foot globe with great accuracy and care. Its construction materials included wood and thin brass plates. It took him twenty-five years to complete this handsome globe, which then became an international attraction.

As time went on, globes became bigger and more elaborate. The one made in 1664 for Frederick, Duke of Holstein-Gottorp, was eleven feet in diameter and weighed three and one-half tons. A circular balcony permitted close observation, and inside the globe, which could be entered through a door, the stars of the heavens were portrayed. The globe itself rotated fully—once every twenty-four hours.

Louis XIV, King of France, joined in the rivalry, and his fifteen-foot globe, made by a Venetian monk, must have gained him top spot in the globe competition for a time, at least. In fact, this terrestrial globe was one of a pair. The other was a celestial globe equally large. Both globes were provided with doors, and each would accommodate thirty people at one time. Such a king as Louis XIV had his globes decorated in an extremely elaborate and costly manner.

Fashions change. In the eighteenth century, many English men of affluence and position carried vest-pocket-sized globes, less than three inches in diameter. But, again in France—in 1824—Colonel Langlois erected a globe in the Champs Élysées in Paris. Its linear scale was such that a one-inch line on the globe represented a line only five miles long on the earth. The diameter of that globe was 128 feet!

Globes, terrestrial and celestial, were used in American colonial colleges long before the Revolution. Every college-educated man of that time had studied a series of exercises done with properly equipped globes. It therefore seems strange that the first globes made in the United States are said not to have been produced until 1810. James Wilson, at one time a Vermont farmer, is currently accorded the title of "America's first globe-maker," but someday, perhaps, evidence will be uncovered to show that globes were made in this country earlier than 1810—possibly even before the War for Independence, when globes were so prominent a part of the "philosophical apparatus" in American colleges.

After reading about geography and exploration and especially after seeing at Dartmouth College, in New Hampshire, a pair of large globes—imported from England, as presumably were all others at that time— Wilson sold his farm stock for $130 and decided to risk his whole future as a globe-maker. So successful was his Bradford, Vermont, venture that he later opened another globe-making factory in Albany, New York.

Today there are a number of excellent globe manufacturers in the United States, and while extremely accurate and beautiful globes are still quite expensive to buy, these manufacturers do also make very adequate globes inexpensive enough for nearly every home. The American Geographical Society, in particular, has produced a remarkable though inexpensive globe utilizing colors in most imaginative ways to present such diverse features as political boundaries and ocean depths.

You really should have a globe of your own, and a good guidebook to show you how to use and understand the globe.

Only on a globe map can the distances, shapes, areas, and directions experienced on the real earth *all* be correctly represented *at the same time*. If one understands scale and angular measurements, he can learn quite a good deal about the relationships among these things for real places on earth. Such knowledge is absolutely essential to anyone wishing to become a geographer.

But, you may ask, if globes are so excellent for the things stated in the preceding paragraph, why would anyone want to use a map produced on a piece of paper, with the distortions that necessarily accompany any attempt to represent any considerable part of a curved surface on a flat one? This is a question that many geographers through the ages have discussed. Ptolemy said, "When the earth is delineated on a sphere, it has a shape like its own, nor is there any need of altering at all." But on a globe that can be readily seen and handled, it isn't easy to provide enough space for all the details desired. And to see the far side, Ptolemy added in effect, either the globe or the observer must be moved.

Thus, since one can put on a piece of paper of any desired size at all a representation of an area from the earth's surface of any size he wishes, the flat map has a flexibility that cannot be duplicated by a globe equally portable. Maps fold up, can easily be reproduced, can be stored conveniently, and can readily be compared side by side or by transparent overlays. All these things are matters of convenience. But there are additional characteristics of maps that make them extremely valuable for scientific purposes, navigation, planning, and other such things. Even though every flat map is distorted, ranging from a negligible amount for maps of small parts of the earth's surface to an extreme amount for very large areas, not every one of the four things mentioned earlier—distances, shapes, areas, and directions—need be distorted on a given map. It is possible, on a map, to show the *size* of areas in the same proportions to each other that they have on the earth's surface. But to do this, *shapes* must be distorted. Similarly, to maintain faithfully certain of the *direction* characteristics of the earth for navigation use, representation of *areas* can be made to absorb all the distortion. Thus, there are many possible ways in which maps can easily be tailored for specific single purposes.

The history of map making is full of the solutions that cartographers and geographers have developed to provide maps for the many general and special purposes for which they are required. These maps were at first developed principally through the use of mathematics for perspective projections, which are those that also represent the geometric reality of actual projection, by lines of sight from a globe onto a surface such as a plane, cone, or cylinder. Note that the plane already is flat, and a cone or cylinder—unlike a sphere—can be simply cut to make it lie flat.

To gain special qualities through the years, cartographers have modified the perspective projections by transpositions or mathematical transformations. There also have been developed purely mathematical projections bearing no simple or direct relationship whatsoever to perspective.

We could not possibly discuss all or even the most important map projections ever designed, but mention of a few of them is in order.

During the second century B.C., in which Crates constructed his globe, Hipparchus is also known to have designed a systematic world map projection, although he did not compile the map. The first important map of the world by a known cartographer was that produced by Anaximander in the seventh century B. C., although clay tablets depicting the known world during the dynasty of Sargon of Akkad (about 2400–2200 B.C.) were found in modern times near Kirkuk in Iraq, and may now be seen in the British Museum in London.

In the second century A.D., Marinus of Tyre constructed a projection showing a latitude and longitude grid.

The man who may have had the greatest influence on cartography of any single individual of all time, Claudius Ptolemy, invented a number of different projections. Virtually all knowledge of the mathematics of map projections was lost to Europeans in the subsequent centuries. The revival of learning, the expansion of trade, and the ocean explorations of the late Middle Ages led to a revival of interest in map projections and the resurrection of Ptolemy's geographical works. This bustle of activity featured one of the world's later most used and misused projections, the Mercator projection of 1568. It was designed for navigational purposes, which it has served well, but its great upper-latitude area expansions—required to permit constant compass headings to be shown everywhere on the map as straight lines—have often led the uninitiated into further confusion or, even worse, unrecognized wrong conclusions about the relations of areas. A person should always try to learn the special properties of any map before he uses it.

Conic projections developed in 1772 by the famous cartographer Lambert are still widely used. Lambert was an extremely active originator of projections, and has many to his credit. Other very famous projections include those of Cassini, Sanson-Flamsteed, Mollweide, Hammer-Aitoff, Briesemeister, and O. M. Miller. The two latter gentlemen are modern cartographers on the staff of the American Geographical Society of New York City.

Not all of cartography can be summed up in terms of the mathematics of map projections. Types of paper, ink, colors, and drawing and scribing tools have all undergone long histories of development. The method for best making maps from aerial photographs is a recently developed and still actively growing branch of cartography. A thrilling and never-ending exercise is found in the joint effort of cartographers and geographers to decide what features are to be shown on any map, and to reach valid conclusions in physical and social science through map-implemented analysis.

But the greatest developments are still to come. Map making is not a dead subject. A number of brilliant young scholars, such as Waldo Tobler and William Bunge, are opening up new vistas daily. For example, electronic computers and automation in relation to cartography are the subject of considerable study. The significance of the map as a data-storage element in a data-processing system is now appreciated. Similarly, the roles of maps as computer inputs and processed outputs are rapidly becoming better understood. But the development of greatest intellectual excitement is the one in which the properties of map projections that expand, collapse, dislocate, repeat, invert, eliminate, interrupt, or superimpose surfaces are being utilized in the forming and testing of geographical theory.

6

The Art of Travel

By 1970, Great Britain and France expect to have in operation on their commercial airlines jet aircraft capable of flying 1,450 miles an hour. These supersonic flying machines will be expected to complete transatlantic crossings from New York to Paris in about two and one-half hours, on a regularly scheduled basis.

Great Britain and France have already reached an agreement to finance the building of such Mach 2 aircraft. (Mach 1 is the speed of sound. This is approximately 660 miles an hour at 35,000 feet. Mach 2 and Mach 3 are two and three times the speed of sound, respectively.)

European nations have been consistently outdone by the Americans in developing high-speed commercial aircraft since World War II. In this period the Atlantic crossing time has been cut from twelve hours to six hours. Not only is there a possibility of crossing times of two and one-half hours by 1970, but very probably there will be crossing times of one and three-quarters hours by about 1974. Planes for the later, Mach 3, flights are already being planned for by United States builders, who apparently have decided to skip the Mach 2 stage entirely. The day when any traveler can, if he wishes, circumnavigate the globe in less than half a day seems astonishingly close at hand.

But who would want to fly so fast? Well, any decrease in travel time is accompanied by an increase in sociological intensity, both as its cause and its effect. Commercial, diplomatic, military, and other passengers —first, because they wish to gain an advantage, but then of necessity from force of competition—will find it increasingly necessary to reduce the time gap that distance imposes between places. What is at first an advantage often in due course becomes a requisite.

But the aforementioned is travel as a business requirement—travel as an instrument for properly discharging one's duties—travel as a necessity. Actually, the subject at hand is travel as an art—not the hurried journeying to get as quickly as possible from one place to another, with little or no regard for what lies in between. Rather, this chapter discusses the geographer's attitude toward travel. To him, travel is not just a disagreeable though unavoidable task, but an opportunity to move about in the world, to see it, to attempt to understand it, and above all to appreciate it.

Perhaps he has in him something more of the wanderer than of what might be called the traveler. At least, the wanderer is often roaming for the sheer love of sampling more of the world's flavor. His destination on any journey may be uncertain, or at any rate it may be something to be reached only when he has fully satisfied himself that he has seen as much as he cares to of all places that lie on his way—and the way itself may be as twisting, as turning, and as overlapping as his whim dictates.

Few of us are such blithe spirits that we would be willing to accept a true wanderer's life with its material privations, its uncertainties, its lack of old age security, and its assumption of the role of social outcast. Even though we may secretly desire such a life very much, the best most of us can hope is that from time to time we may indulge ourselves in a "get-away-from-it-all" vacation.

But, whether we travel long distances or short, we can all learn to gain greater advantage from our moving about. A person may visit a new place with no previous knowledge of its nature; all that he sees and hears there will be novel. The excitement of such a visit will come from the sheer satisfaction of picturesque sights, beautiful scenery, and appealing peoples—or the opposites of these things. All that is encountered will be seen and understood on its own terms alone. A small child who can have no great store of knowledge sees the world in much this way. Even for adults, it is not an entirely inadequate way to travel. A person forms his own impressions, not shaped in advance by others; there is no danger here of actuality failing to live up to expectation. Impressions thus freely formed remain vivid and personal. Yet enjoyments of this sort are primitive, and if one has any intellectual and scholarly inclinations at all, such experiences are not completely satisfying.

To build up meaning from the experiences of travel requires comparison and relation: only as facts are related to other facts do they take on real significance. An intelligent traveler, therefore, will wish to read about and study in advance the places he is to visit. And then, upon return, he will attempt to fit what he has observed into the pattern of all his other understandings of the world.

But the author does not intend to make travel seem like a forbidding experience by presenting a scholarly treatise on the collection, selection, analysis, and synthesis of information. Instead, he would like to point out a few ways in which any person, by expanding his own powers of observation, can add enjoyment to his traveling, be it necessary or relaxing.

Most of us are blessed with senses in good working order. It is through these senses and these alone that we gain information about the real world. When properly organized by intelligence, the experiences of the senses can become a wonderful source of comfort, enjoyment, and satisfaction.

The late Harold Gatty was a marine and air navigator who thoroughly understood, used, and improved the highly advanced technical aids of his profession. But he also took extraordinary care to record an enormous number of his own and other men's experiences in pathfinding simply by observing nature through the senses.

To explain the ways in which early explorers and primitive tribes were able to engage in long journeys by directly observing nature, Gatty drew on years of personal practice and on the accounts of others. Whether you yourself travel to remote central Asia or merely walk about your own neighborhood, you will find more pleasure in either activity if you learn, as did the Australian-born Harold Gatty, to observe and understand such phenomena as birds, animal life, weather, vegetation, storms, and the positions of the sun, the stars, and the moon.

More and more, people are becoming city dwellers, and their lives no longer depend as they once did on seeing and knowing nature's signs. Well-marked roads, public transportation, or the professional trip-planner's advice now guide us on our journeys. Because seemingly trivial details of nature are no longer vital to us, the habit of their observation and interpretation is in danger of decay, though they still are of paramount importance to many of the world's peoples. But, as Gatty suggested, there is no more reason for this decay than for that of "music, painting, bird watching, tobogganing, or any other form of pure art, science, or sport." The habit of "natural observation, of noticing natural features, is one that can easily be developed with proper training and practice—developed to such a pitch that astonishing feats can be performed without conscious mental effort."

Such practice not only affords much pleasure to the ordinary individual, but can in some cases be the means to survival for the lost camper, the marooned sailor, or the airplane pilot and his passengers forced down in the wilderness.

For those persons who are abroad at night for whatever reasons, the moon and stars are a means of traveling with certainty in reasonably clear weather. While for an accurate mathematical method of position-finding a navigator must make careful observations on the celestial bodies with precision instruments, even unaided inspection of the night sky can be of value and interest to the nonprofessional.

The moon, as is well known, shines only by reflecting the light of the sun (and to a very much lesser degree that of other bodies). Thus the moon can show the sun's direction even when the sun is below the horizon. At any one time, half the moon is light and half of it is dark. Because the moon always presents almost the same face to the earth, the part of the illuminated surface we see varies through the month from nothing at all, through a waxing crescent, to a full moon and back again.

The center of the moon's changing light hemisphere always faces directly toward the sun, and if we can visualize where this center is we can deduce the sun's position.

From the point of view of the earthbound observer, the full moon is always directly opposite the sun. Thus the full moon rises as the sun sets, and sets as the sun rises. It reaches its highest point in the heavens at approximately midnight.

About a week later, the waning half-moon rises at midnight, reaches its highest point at sunrise, and sets at noon. In yet another week the moon will be "new" and not seen by earth's inhabitants.

On the average, the moon rises and sets about fifty minutes later each night. Thus, to go from the thinnest crescent just after new moon to the waxing half-moon (or first quarter) requires about a week. There is a perfect full moon approximately seven days later. From full moon to waning half-moon (last quarter) again takes slightly over a week. This recurring cycle runs to new moon again in another week. Altogether, the complete change of the moon's phases takes about twenty-nine and a half days.

Knowledge of the moon's behavior will allow the night traveler to estimate how much moonlight he may depend on (in fair weather) during the particular time of his trip. Directions, too, can be found from the moon.

For the observer in the Northern Hemisphere's middle and upper latitudes, the moon is always due south when it is highest in the sky. For the full moon, this point is reached, of course, around midnight, and for the three-week-old waning half-moon, at sunrise. But even when the moon is not at its highest point, one can still get a general indication of a north-south line on earth, for an imaginary line through the tips of the horns of the crescent moon will always be more or less north and south. And if the crescent moon is a waxing one, lying, as it always does, close behind the sun, the horns themselves will point toward the east. In like fashion, the horns of the old crescent waning moon leading the sun across the sky will point toward the west.

The stars, but not the planets, stay always in the same relation to one another. Thus, night after night for the observer in one place, the stars trace the same fixed paths across the sky, as the earth rotates. But although the sequences in which the various stars pass over different places on the earth remain unchanged, the times do not. Because stars rise three minutes and fifty-six seconds earlier each night, the heavenly panorama displayed each evening changes constantly through the seasons.

If you have ever watched the stars with care throughout an evening or have examined cleverly produced time-exposure photographs of the heavens, you may have noticed that the stars seem to move as on a giant wheel about a certain fixed point.

This fixed point will be high or low in the sky, depending on where you are. If you live in the northern part of the United States, the point lies due north of you, about halfway up in the sky from the horizon toward the point directly overhead, called the zenith. The altitude of the celestial pole (the fixed point about which the heavens turn) is measured in degrees and is always equal to the latitude of the place where the observation is made. Thus, the north celestial pole lies directly above the north geographical pole.

Fortunately, almost exactly at the position of the north celestial pole there is a star. It has been named Polaris naturally enough, and is often called the Pole, or North, Star. So very small is the circle that this star traces about the celestial pole that explorers, navigators, travelers, and wanderers are able to rely on it as a virtually constant direction-indicator.

Since the stars retain fixed spatial patterns with regard to each other, you can learn to identify many of them by means of a pointer system based on certain very easily recognized constellations such as the Big Dipper and Orion. The stars Dubhe and Mirak, on the outside edge of the bowl of the Big Dipper, are lined up in a way that points toward the Pole Star.

The stars, appearing as they do to revolve about the poles of the heavens, provide an extremely accurate means of time determination when measured by appropriately sensitive instruments. The casual traveler, too, can use the stars for time telling in a rough way. Several methods exist. If you live in an area where the stars of the Big Dipper do not go below the horizon, one of the most interesting and easily used methods requires only that you imagine a clockface with positions one to twelve marked on it in the conventional way. Let six be at the horizon down from the Pole Star. Twelve is toward the zenith. Of course then, three will be on the right hand toward the east when you face toward the Pole Star, and nine will be on the left hand toward the west.

Begin by noting the Pole Star and the line from it through the pointer stars, Dubhe and Mirak. Visualize

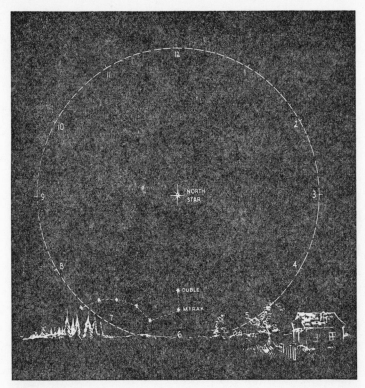

Telling time on the star clock (see text).

Cape May, New Jersey
October 5, 1963

Line from the Pole, or North, Star points to
6 hours on star clock.
12 − 6 = 6.
2 × 6 = 12
12 + 11 = 23 hours (Local Star Time on 24-hour basis).
March 23 to September 23 = 6 months.
6 × 2 = 12 hours.
September 23 to October 5 = 12 days.
4 × 12 = 48 minutes.
Total correction = 12 hours 48 minutes.
23 hours −12 hours 48 minutes =
10.12 P.M. Local Standard Time.

the hour number on the star clock to which this line points. Subtract this hour number from twelve. Multiply the answer by two, and add eleven. This result is known as local star time. To convert it to the local civil time of the place, the following correction is needed.

From the answer you have just found, subtract two hours for each full month that the date of observation falls after March 23 as the beginning date. Allow also a four-minute deduction for each day of any remaining part of a month. Thus, by rough observation of the Big Dipper alone, you may arrive at a fairly accurate indication of the local standard time.

Of course, the problem of extremely accurate time measurement and timekeeping is a difficult one. Perhaps the simplest kind of time that man has kept through the ages is sun time. An apparent solar day is the time from when we see the sun exactly on our meridian until we see it there again the next day. For people living in the United States, the sun is always due south when it passes over the meridian of longitude for any place. Thus, if you put a stake in the ground, the shadow will always fall due north when it is noon by the sun. If you have earlier established a north-south line by reference to Polaris, you can use this to check sun-time noon. If, however, you also have an accurate mechanical timepiece you will find that not exactly twenty-four hours elapse between each successive meridian crossing of the sun. There is a variation in the speed at which the earth moves on its orbit around the sun, and this, when combined with the earth's rotation, results in a variation in the length of the apparent solar day. The actual differences at times amount to nearly as much as seventeen minutes longer or shorter than the average length of the solar day.

In order to avoid the variations that occur in apparent solar time, we assume the mean, i.e., average, length of a solar day as our standard and divide it exactly into twenty-four equal hours, which our mechanical timekeeping devices are designed to indicate.

If every one of our mechanical clocks were set to the exact mean solar time of the place where it is located, no two of these clocks would agree unless they were keeping the time for places exactly on the same meridian of longitude. (It goes without saying, of course, that both clocks would have to be accurate timekeepers, too.) In order to overcome all the great inconveniences associated with a time system where any two places would differ in time if they differed in longitude, a system of time zones has been established. In the United States, there are four such broad zones. Thus, for people in the eastern states the standard time is always three hours later than for those on the Pacific Coast.

With practice, you can learn to estimate time quite well by observing the sun's position. The sun rises exactly in the east and sets exactly to the west on only two days during the year. These days generally fall on March 21 and September 22. During the spring and summer, people in the United States see the sun rise north of east and set north of west. In the fall and

109

winter, sunrise and sunset occur south of east and west respectively. Of course, this means also that the noonday sun will appear much higher in the sky at the start of summer than it does at winter's beginning.

Observing and learning of the seasonal variation in the sun's altitudes and directions is a source of pleasure, and might someday be valuable to you. For example, you can use the sun or the shadows it casts to maintain a given course while walking. For the middle latitudes, a fairly useful—though very rough—generalization is that the sun changes its direction about 15° an hour. Of course, a mathematical solution for precise values exists, and these values may be ascertained exactly at any time throughout the year. And, as is the case with many other kinds of information used by geographers, astronomers, and navigators, precomputed tables of certain values exist to make the task of figuring easier.

For your own instruction and enjoyment, why don't you sometime drive a stake perpendicularly into the ground and try the following little experiment? If you observe the shadow that the stick makes, you will learn some interesting things.

Make a mark on the ground where the end of the shadow lies early in the morning. Repeat this mark frequently during the whole daylight period; perhaps six times will be enough, if the intervals are fairly evenly spaced. You can then make a smooth curve on the ground to connect all the marks you have made at the shadow's end. You will see that not all parts of this curve are equally distant from the stake. In fact, the shadow of the stake will be shortest at noon (apparent

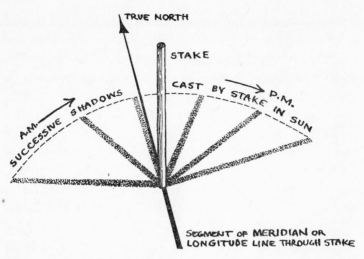

Finding a true north-south line by means of a stake and its shadows (see text).

sun time). Now if you find the point on the smooth curve that is closest to the stake, and connect this point to the stake itself by a straight line, this latter line will be a true north-south line. Hence, you will have drawn on the earth itself a line representing a tiny arc of the imaginary meridian of longitude passing through that place.

You can also draw this segment of a line of longitude in another way. Again, drive a stake into the ground, but now draw several concentric circles around it. Watch the shadow from the stake as it is produced by the sun in the morning. When the end of the shadow just touches any one of these circles, mark that point. In the afternoon, note the point where the shadow again touches that very same circle. By means of a

111

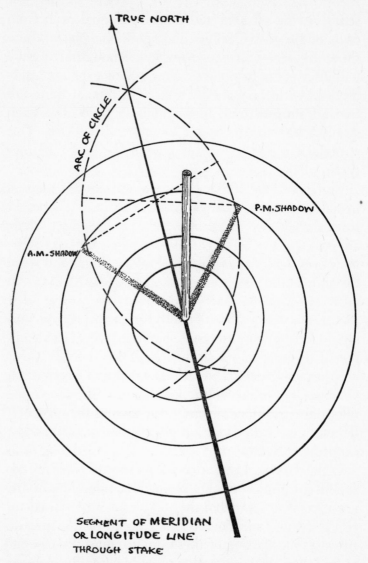

TRUE NORTH

ARC OF CIRCLE

P.M. SHADOW

A.M. SHADOW

SEGMENT OF MERIDIAN
OR LONGITUDE LINE
THROUGH STAKE

Another way of finding a north-south line (see text).

string, swing off arcs with long but equal radii from each of these two points and mark the place where these arcs cross. If you draw long enough arcs, they will intersect in two places. Now connect the arc intersections with the stake by a straight line. If there are two arc intersections, they will both be on the same straight line as the stake, as you will notice. This straight line also represents part of the longitude meridian of the place.

The directional influences of the sun can be observed in nature in a number of ways. The basic shapes of trees throughout the world, for example, often show adaptations to the angle of the sun's rays. Locally, moreover, one may observe the effect of sun and wind through noting the modification of basic shapes. Almost everyone has seen windswept trees, or at least pictures of them. Where the wind is strong and persistently from one general direction, vegetation will reveal this circumstance.

Trees often show more foliage and a greater development of branches on their sunnier side. Flowering plants also can be observed to bloom at different times, depending on the slope on which they stand and the exposure it has.

On a dark night or a very foggy day, one can use sounds to guide himself. Especially important is the use of echoes. Someday it may be of importance for you to know that it takes sound about five seconds to travel a mile. Travelers have often used this knowledge to find their distance from a mountainside. In many of the fjord areas of the world, captains of small vessels, using stopwatches and whistles, take advantage of the echo system of navigation to help steer safe channels during fog or darkness.

As you know, light travels so very fast that we can in our ordinary experiences regard its transmission and reception as instantaneous. The next time you see a lightning flash, time the interval between it and the thunderclap that follows. Do this several times and you will be able to estimate whether or not the storm is moving nearer to you.

If you ever travel widely about the world, you will later recall many special sights and sounds. But doubtless, smells will remain among your most vivid impressions. Travelers lost in desert areas have reported being able to find oases because the smells from camels stopping at these spots were recognizable many, many miles before they could be seen.

Similarly, searchers hunting for a meat cache in the Arctic are likely to follow the well-known practice of deliberately heading a little downwind, and then "homing in," as it were, by scent.

Many sea captains have reported from the South Seas that certain islands have their own smells, which can often be picked up before the land is sighted. Certain tropical flowers especially are exceedingly fragrant.

As indicators, seamen have often used to great advantage the flights of seabirds—their numbers, kinds, and the directions in which they are traveling. The greatest of all early maritime peoples, the primitive Polynesians, as well as the early Irish and Viking

114

sailors, seem surely to have utilized bird migrations as visible aids for their exploratory journeys. Perhaps the Polynesians, who had no compasses, were able to explore a trackless Pacific realm of seven million square miles by observing migrating birds season after season until they were certain where a consistent flyway existed, and by then following it to new land.

Hundreds of other examples might also be given to show how man can make use of nature's signs. Every cloud formation has a story to tell. Many airmen have found small islands in vast oceans because of certain peculiarities in the clouds above them, which have revealed their locations. The ability quickly to recognize clues such as these proved precious to many American fliers during World War II.

Wherever you go, whether in densely populated areas, open country, or true deserts, try to observe all there is to be observed. Make full use of all your senses. Practice, and you will improve. Note the change in the landscape from season to season. Pay attention to details. Let no travel be wasted—whether it be a neighborhood walk to buy a newspaper, or a long sea journey to a remote island. Every inch of the way is filled with something new that you have not yet discovered, no matter how many times you may have traveled that way before.

Geographers love to travel, and their work often affords them the opportunity to do so. Whether they work at abstruse theories in macrogeography, serve their country in the diplomatic corps, design new mathematical map projections, or teach in schools and col-

115

leges, all geographers share alike their enjoyment of
unhurried travel, the leisurely inspection of details,
and the attempt to put the details together into a
meaningful whole.

Even when geographers are not traveling, they
spend much of their spare time looking at maps and
atlases, planning where they would like to go next if
they should have the chance.

Among his many other accomplishments, Harold
Gatty accompanied the aviator Wiley Post as navigator
on the celebrated round-the-world flight of the "Winnie
Mae" in 1931.

After that record-breaking eight-day flight, Gatty
and Post spent five months flying on a good-will tour,
crisscrossing the United States and visiting about a
town a day. While flying at low altitudes, Gatty fa-
miliarized himself with the country below, paying
special attention to the features not generally shown
on conventional maps. Among other things, he observed types of vegetation, kinds and patterns of crops,
the layout of farms and farm buildings, the architecture
of houses and public buildings, field boundaries, and
road networks.

As Gatty once noted, not everybody is lucky enough
to be able to see the country from the air, and to follow
its changing personality over a great continent. Clearly
his early North American flights taught him much
about the value of exercising awareness. Indeed, after
practicing his observations, he found that in quite a
short time he was able to recognize a locality almost
anywhere in the United States without consulting his

116

map. However, "to read the personality of a country-side like this, it is not invariably necessary to leave the comfort of one's own home. If you cannot for the time being study scenery from the air, from a railroad train, or car, you must study photographs," urged Gatty.

A great deal of enjoyment can be had from studying the details of a scenic picture. Cover the caption and see if you can tell the locality. What is the season? In what directions do roads lie? How can you tell? How are the buildings oriented? Why? What time of day is it? Can you see evidences of prevailing winds? The more questions you try to answer, the more questions you will think of asking. In that way your knowledge will be broadened and deepened, and your satisfactions and enjoyments will be increased when you do get the opportunity to travel.

Study pictures, read more, and whenever possible go out and look around you. There is never any reason to be bored with the world. There is always something new to be seen, understood, and appreciated.

Learn the art of travel, not just the routine of taking trips.

117

7

Should You Become a Geographer?

Professional geographers are a fortunate group of people; perhaps more than any other professionals, they are happy in their work. Their adult geographical endeavors are but the refined and sophisticated expression of delightful interests and inquisitive concerns that began in childhood. Almost to a person, professional geographers admit that as children they loved travel and adventure stories, were curious about many aspects of the places around them, and followed hobbies related to geography, such as stamp collecting. But among all the geographers-to-be, the most common trait was a special feeling for maps. Any young person who is fascinated by maps is a potential geographer. Whether your concern is for the mathematical

118

projection of maps, the compiling of original maps, the study and comparison of existing maps, or the contemplation of maps' artistic qualities, here you have an interest that might well make you want to consider geography as a profession.

Many professional geographers did not actually decide on geography as their career until they were well along with their formal academic training. As often as not, they decided to become geographers only at the beginning of graduate college. With maturity, and after they had been exposed to a wide variety of academic disciplines, they realized that in geography they could neatly combine many otherwise separate interests and skills, and that at the same time they could satisfy some of their longstanding wishes.

In geography there is room for people of diverse talents, and there is need for them, too. For some individuals, the physical world is the most important topic. Other individuals are interested especially in social and economic phenomena. To one person, writing offers the greatest satisfaction. Another revels in mathematical analysis. All can find a place in geography.

The "compleat geographer" exists only as an ideal. The subject of geography is now extremely broad. All aspects of it have recently opened out tremendously as a result of intensive research, and at present many highly developed specializations exist which only a short time ago were scarcely thought of. But while geography as a subject is expanding into a well-integrated whole, this very enlargement lessens the

119

likelihood that one person ever again will be a complete master of it all.

Even though mastery of the entire field of geography now lies beyond the competence of any individual, however, the course of study for a would-be geographer should probably be organized with the "compleat geographer" in mind. If you are a young person who feels that he or she might like to enter this profession, perhaps you would like to learn more of what is required as an education. Then, if your native talents and the things you take pleasure in seem to point to geography as a likely career, and if the education a geographer must undertake appeals to you, you will probably wish to consider again the kinds of positions geographers can expect to fill. On the basis of all these considerations you can then hope to reach a decision.

Now, what education might help a person prepare himself to become a professional geographer?

Almost all elementary and secondary school students are bound to a certain few prescribed plans of general education. If you hope one day to become a professional geographer, you will most certainly wish, if you are able, to take the college preparatory course in secondary school so that you can go on to college. A college degree has become very nearly an absolute necessity for anyone aiming at a responsible position in geography. In fact, graduate degrees are now required of applicants, for consideration for most positions. Educational specialization in geography largely occurs at the college graduate level, and many advisers

120

feel that such late specialization is ideal, with the earlier years given over to a truly well-rounded liberal education.

A young person who has definitely decided quite early that he wants a career in geography can do a number of things to help himself within the prescribed curriculum of the secondary school. If geography courses are actually offered within the college preparatory program, the student should by all means enroll in some of them. But even when no such direct courses are offered, a surprising number of options can be exercised that will help lead to the goal.

For example, often in English literature courses, books to be read may be selected from a very broad list. In some cases, students even have full freedom to select their reading, with the teacher's final approval as the only requirement. In either event, pupils can in all probability choose works that are travel narratives, or are excellent descriptions of various parts of the world. In writing reports and compositions, students may also gain an opportunity to strengthen their knowledge and understanding of descriptive geography. They can accomplish the same aim, too, by carefully planning outside readings and extra-credit reports in other courses such as history. Every well-educated person is expected to be familiar with the world in more or less general geographic terms. The individual who wishes to be a geographer should take advantage of every opportunity the curriculum offers to make himself even more aware of these things than is the well-educated person who specializes in some

121

other subject. Read, read, read. Learn about the world.

Descriptive geography is, of course, only one phase of geographic endeavor. Also important are geography at the level of classification and geography at the level of prediction.

Although geographic classification is built upon that one factor that is peculiarly geographic—that is, location—much that is taught about classification in connection with other secondary school courses is pertinent. Any student who has learned something of the nature of the problems and methods of classification in one science will later find his knowledge of great value in connection with the geographical classification we call regionalization.

To do regional geography well, the embryonic geographer will at some later time require formal instruction in the specifics of this branch of geography. When that time comes, he will find it valuable to have paid attention to the methods of classification developed in such courses as chemistry or botany. Then too, much of the new mathematics in the schools is organized in terms of set theory. Elementary statistics courses are now being offered to more of the younger students than ever before. The operations in set theory, and certain of the ideas in rudimentary statistical analysis, are closely linked with classification. More and more, geographers are recognizing the importance of these operations and ideas for regional geography. Increasingly, advanced instruction in geography will come to capitalize on students' early exposure to such concepts.

Many of the branches of mathematics are coming to have ever greater significance for predictive geography. The various geometries—including plane, perspective, and especially spherical—can be studied profitably. Their logical sequels, plane trigonometry and spherical trigonometry, are exceptionally valuable, too. So also is topology, for the strength it provides in the study of the geography of trade routes, communication networks, highway systems, international boundaries, and so on. At the level of predictive geography, all these branches of mathematics are important, as also are analytic geometry, the various algebras, and the differential and integral calculus. Of course, not all these courses can be taken in secondary school. Many will be taken in college.

In the academic curriculum, other courses are offered which traditionally have been linked with geography, and for good reason. If you take courses that teach something about climates, landforms, soils, vegetation, and geological formations, you will receive instruction important to you as a prospective geographer. Sometimes the various history and social studies courses that are offered are of great assistance. If the geography of one particular part of the world interests you especially, you might wish to select the appropriate foreign language to study.

Not only in school, but outside it as well, you can pursue activities designed to help you reach your goal. The exercise of your powers of observation in the world about you is a fine thing. (See again, Chapter 6, *The Art of Travel.*) Of course, your outside reading

123

can be arranged constructively, too. In all you read and experience, look for the ways in which various things are related one to another, and try to develop understandings of these associations. Above all, pay attention to the nature and detail of all maps you encounter, both inside the classroom and out of it.

I am often asked by young students what they should study in college if they want to become geographers later on. Only in very rare instances do I tell them that they should undertake a course of study other than the general liberal arts program at a good college. It is absolutely essential that they have a wide range of knowledge and a firm base of many viewpoints before they undertake in graduate school the extremely intensive specialization in geographical study alone. I would even go so far as to say that, rather than take a great number of regional geography courses beyond the introductory undergraduate course and perhaps one or two additional introductory regional courses, a student would be better advised to use his elective options for preparation in philosophy, the humanities, literature, scientific method, mathematics, history, or foreign languages.

I have already mentioned that it is advisable fully to develop a foreign language, in anticipation of a later "area specialization." If the potential geographer is interested in the history of geographic thought, he might do well to study the classical languages also, so that he will have Greek and Latin adequate to undertake someday, if he wishes, truly original scholarly

124

research in ancient and medieval geographic thought and presentation.

At the college undergraduate level, other courses outside geography can be taken to advantage by the would-be geographer. In each of these courses, selected requirements for outside reading, reports, and term papers may be fulfilled not only to satisfy immediate assignments, but also with a possible future career as a geographer in mind. For instance, in economics courses, special study of location theory can perhaps be undertaken. Any good economic geographer these days must be well versed in the theory of location of economic activity. And, of course, location theory in economics cannot be comprehended without a firm knowledge of the bases of trade. To bring together these branches, general price theory is required. Having taken these courses, the prospective economic geographer may wish to elect additional work in economics and, where they are available, he might consider marketing and transportation courses. But the geographer-to-be must guard against early overspecialization. In his undergraduate career he must make sure that he obtains a broadly based liberal education, in which he can become familiar with the principal ideas in as many of the major fields of knowledge as possible—especially in those fields that act as links among the various disciplines.

Thus, while a prospective political geographer may wish to take more than one pertinent course in political science, he probably should not allow himself to use up all his electives in that single field. Similarly, geol-

125

ogy will tempt the physical geographer, and botany the biogeographer. Prospective geographers, like all other scholars-to-be, should utilize their undergraduate days to acquire the general liberal education that will help them subsequently to keep their intensive specialization of study and their narrower research inquiries always in proper perspective.

All the advice given above relates to the development of the intellect and the organization of knowledge within one's mind. Sir Francis Bacon once wrote to the effect that reading and study make a *full* man. He added, however, that speaking makes a *ready* man, and writing an *exact* man.

In your undergraduate education you should also keep these two latter aims in mind. It will avail society little for you to become a full person who cannot or will not also communicate his knowledge in a ready and exact manner. You therefore should be sure to include public speaking, debating, or other courses related to oral presentation, thinking on your feet, and providing ready responses. The exact presentation of your acquired knowledge in written form is even more important. Here, courses in preparing carefully organized, well presented, and thoroughly documented reports are essential. If you can learn to combine these necessary features with fine exposition and a good writing style, you will be an accomplished person indeed.

In graduate college, intense specialization will begin. Fullness, readiness, and exactness will still be matters of great concern, but for those students who wish to go on to a career as a professional geographer, this concern will be focused especially on the subject of geography.

In preparing for a Master's degree, they will be expected to study and understand the major ideas within the subject of geography. Its concepts and its methods, rules, and procedures will be stressed. Of course, attention will be given to regional facts, and at this level of education the degree candidate may place emphasis on some regional specialization of his choice. Generally, however, it is the regional *concept* that is emphasized rather than any specific region. Climatology, geomorphology, cartography, mathematical and statistical analysis, and other related subjects may be studied within the framework of geographical thought. In addition to examinations in individual courses, a general comprehensive examination will usually have to be passed and a Master's thesis written, in order to obtain a degree.

For those who wish to go on to the degree of Doctor of Philosophy (Ph.D.) in geography, additional courses are required. Additional ideas are explored, this time at the theoretical level. The emphasis is upon the means of integrating knowledge within the field, but at the same time the student usually picks some topic or region of special interest which he wishes to study and about which he feels qualified to do original and intensive research.

Before the student is allowed to engage in this research problem of his own, he is required to demonstrate his command over the whole subject of

127

geography and to show his preparation and ability to do original research, by passing another quite long series of written examinations (as many as twelve hours). These are called "the preliminary examinations"; "preliminary" here refers to the subsequent research program. In addition, reading examinations in two foreign languages must be passed. French and German long have been the required pair, but increasingly now other languages are acceptable when they are clearly related to whatever regional interest the candidate may have.

Having survived the preliminaries, the geographer-to-be now sets out upon his own research program. He will collect information, analyze it thoroughly, and present the results in the form of a Ph.D. dissertation. This work may take from several years, at least, to perhaps a decade, in some cases. Throughout this period the candidate will be in contact with a senior faculty member who will act in a supervisory capacity. In addition to fullness and exactness, the research and its presentation must show originality. Ideally the dissertation will represent a true advancement of knowledge.

When the dissertation has been completed, it will be submitted to a board of perhaps five readers who come from senior faculty not only within the field of geography but outside it as well. Each member of the board will study the dissertation, to make certain that it meets the general standards of the graduate college as well as those of the specific academic disciplines involved.

When the candidate has met the requirements of the supervisor and the dissertation readers, and they have attested to his fullness and exactness, his final readiness is determined by an oral examination, which includes the oral defense of his dissertation. This process usually centers at first on the major thesis and conclusions of the dissertation, but then goes on to examine how well and quickly the candidate can fit his particular knowledge of the topic he has so long worked with into broader and more general intellectual considerations.

Needless to say, not all those who five or more years earlier may have aspired to the Ph.D. in geography will attain it. The intellectual difficulty, the long time required, the drudgery, the hard work, the not inconsiderable financial expense, and numerous unforeseeable problems all take their toll. If a person is to persevere, his anticipations of the rewards of a career in professional geography must be great enough to overcome the obstacles involved. To gain teaching experience and to help meet the expenses of achieving the doctorate, many young scholars obtain positions as full- or part-time instructors or assistants in the undergraduate college, while they themselves are graduate students. While this generally adds to the time required to reach the Ph.D., the experience and financial help may later turn out to have been critical factors in shaping a career.

What are those probable rewards of a career as a professional geographer which will cause students to persevere? First of all, career geographers are profes-

129

sional people. For many, there is great satisfaction in this. Geographers live a life of service to their fellow-men, and they know they make important contributions to society.

As professional people, they will earn incomes substantially above average, although of course their prospects of great wealth are remote. Most geographers become college teachers. As they gain advancement, their income grows, and their security increases with the accumulation of retirement, hospitalization, and other benefits. Academic life can be very pleasant. The surroundings are attractive, and the company of other faculty members and eager students can be most agreeable.

But, as we have seen, geographers increasingly are coming to hold positions other than those in the academic field. Scientific and cultural societies, business, industry, government, and many other organizations now provide opportunities in which geographers of varied interests, skills, and dispositions can lead happy and purposeful lives.

Because of their education and abilities, geographers frequently are asked to assist in projects that require extensive domestic and foreign travel, or they qualify for fellowships, grants, or awards that make such travel financially easier. Anyone who strongly wishes to travel, and especially anyone who wishes to travel in a meaningful as well as an enjoyable way, should definitely consider a career as a professional geographer. Great satisfaction comes from knowing that you are doing as work what you would do in any case as a hobby; that it affords your family a good living; and especially that yours is a life of service.

Should you become a geographer? No one can really tell you without knowing of your interests, your intelligence, your disposition, your aptitudes, your determination, and your goals in life. If the various job requirements a geographer must meet, the kinds of positions a geographer holds, and the rewards a career in geography offers all appeal to you as they have been described in this short book, why not try to write to or speak with a professional geographer? Your teachers or counselors can help you do this.

In a geographer, one nearly always finds a person in whom his vocation and one of his avocations are the same. Geographers achieve some degree of satisfaction in life.

UNITED STATES GOVERNMENT OFFICES WHICH EMPLOY PROFESSIONAL GEOGRAPHERS (From: *Status and Trends of Geography in the United States, 1957–1960.* Association of American Geographers, 1961.)

Department of Agriculture:
Agricultural Marketing Service; Agricultural Research Service; Foreign Agricultural Service; Forest Service; Rural Electrification Administration; Soil Conservation Service

Atomic Energy Agency:
Division of Raw Materials

Central Intelligence Agency:
Various offices

Department of Commerce:
Business and Defense Services Administration: Office of Area Development; Office of Distribution; Office of Industrial Mobilization; Industry Division

Bureau of the Census: Coordinator for International Statistics; Foreign Manpower Research Office; Geography Division; Industry Division

Other Offices of Department of Commerce: Coast and Geodetic Survey; Bureau of Foreign Commerce; Bureau of Public Roads (Office of Research); Weather Bureau (Office of Climatology)

Department of the Air Force:
Assistant Chief of Staff: Intelligence (Targets, Estimates, etc.)

Deputy Chief of Staff: Operations

132

Aeronautical Chart and Information Center (St. Louis, Missouri)

Air Research and Development Command

Air Force Academy (Colorado Springs, Colorado)

Air University (Montgomery, Alabama)

Department of the Navy:

Hydrographic Office: Planning Division and Technical and Production Department

Office of Naval Research: Geography Branch in the Earth Science Division

Office of Naval Intelligence: Coast and Landing Beach Unit in the Foreign Branch

Executive Office of the President:

Bureau of the Budget: Resources and Civil Works Division

Civil and Defense Mobilization: Contributions Division; Education Division; Research and Development Division

General Services Administration:

Cartographic Records Branch of National Archives

Department of Health, Education, and Welfare:

Office of Education: Division of State and Local Schools and Division of International Education

Public Health Service: Water Supply and Water Pollution Control Division

Department of the Army:

Office of the Chief of Staff: Area Analysis Branch; Technical Division; Directorate of Research and Development

Office of the Chief of Engineers: Intelligence Branch; Army Map Service: Cartographic Di-

133

vision; Engineer Strategic Intelligence Division; Photogrammetric Division; Technical Services Division (Library and Map Evaluation Branch)

Beach Erosion Board

Other Sections of the Department of the Army: Photographic Interpretation Center (Fort Holabird, Maryland); Quartermaster Intelligence Agency; Quartermaster Environmental Research Laboratory (Natick, Massachusetts); Office of the Chief, U.S. Army Transportation Intelligence Agency

Housing and Home Finance Agency:

Urban Renewal Administration; Planning and Engineering Branch

Department of the Interior:

Office of Geography (including Board on Geographic Names)

Technical Review Staff

Geological Survey; Military Geology Branch and Topographic Division

Fish and Wildlife Service

Bureau of Indian Affairs

Bureau of Land Management

Bureau of Mines

National Park Service: Division of Recreation and Resource Planning

Bureau of Reclamation: Division of Project Development and Division of Foreign Activities

International Cooperation Administration:

Program Planning; Industry Division; Community Development Division; Regional Office; individual technicians

Department of Labor:
Bureau of Employment Security
Library of Congress:
Legislative Reference Service
Air Research Division
Map Division
National Science Foundation:
Miscellaneous
Smithsonian Institution:
United States National Museum
Department of State:
Office of the Geographer
Office of the Coordinator of Maps
Bureau of Inter-American Affairs
Bureau of European Affairs
Bureau of Far Eastern Affairs
Bureau of Near Eastern and Southern Asian Affairs
Foreign Service
Tennessee Valley Authority:
Office of Engineering; Division of Water Control;
Maps and Surveys Branch (Chattanooga, Tennessee)
United States Information Agency:
Miscellaneous

Glossary

The terms defined here should not necessarily be considered as representatives of the entire subject of geography, but rather as aids to the reading of this particular book.

CARTOGRAPHY   The art and science of map making.

CHOROGRAPHY   In ancient times this term referred to the study of large regions. (*See also* Topography and Geography.)

CLIMATOLOGY   The study of the earth's climates.

CONTOUR LINE   A line drawn on a map, joining all places at the same elevation. The horizontal spacings on the map among a family of such lines (when a constant vertical interval is maintained)

136

are inversely proportional to the gradients. While contour lines themselves refer to physical landforms, the concept of a family of such lines has been used to portray geographical variations in the values of a wide range of phenomena both for physical and human geography, such as terrestrial magnetism (*isogonic lines*), barometric pressure (*isobars*), temperature (*isotherms*), and potential of population (*isopotentials of population*).

DENSITY OF POPULATION   The average number of persons per unit area within a region.

EQUATOR   The imaginary line on the earth's surface lying midway throughout its entire length between the North Pole and the South Pole.

GEOGRAPHY   The art and science of describing, classifying, and predicting the distribution of phenomena on the earth. The causes, consequences, and interrelationships of the locations of phenomena are especially important in this subject which treats equally well physical, biological, and human factors. Many different specialties exist within geography, such as systematic, regional, physical, human, economic, political, and so on. In ancient times, geography dealt with the whole earth, as contrasted to topography and chorography.

GEOMORPHOLOGY   The study of landforms. Attention is paid to the structures of the earth's crust and

137

the processes by which these structures are changed.

GLOBE   A terrestrial globe is a scale model of the earth.

GRADIENT   On a surface the average gradient between isolines is their vertical interval divided by the horizontal distance between them, measured along a line at right angles to each isoline. The actual gradient at a point is determined by means of the differential calculus. Geographers study gradients relating to the geographical distributions of many kinds of phenomena. Included among these are landform, pressure, temperature, potential of population, space-time, and many other kinds of gradients.

GREAT CIRCLE   A circle on the surface of a sphere formed by the intersection of that surface with a plane passed through the center of that sphere. There are thus an infinite number of great circles possible on the sphere's surface, and all of these bisect each other. The shortest distance between any two points on a truly spherical earth would be the arc of a great circle passing through both of them. Two opposing meridians of longitude form a great circle. Parallels of latitude, except for the Equator, are not great circles.

HEMISPHERE   Half of the earth's surface. The boundary of a hemisphere is a great circle. Thus, the

Equator divides the earth's surface into a Northern and Southern Hemisphere. The prime meridian and the 180° meridian together separate an Eastern from a Western Hemisphere. A great many other kinds of special hemispheres have been defined. Think about the hemisphere centered on your own home.

LATITUDE   The distance of a place on the earth's surface north or south of the Equator, expressed in angular measure based on the earth's center. A degree of latitude on a spherical earth would be everywhere the same length.

LONGITUDE   The distance east and west of the prime meridian, expressed as the angle formed by the plane through a place and the North and South poles with the plane of the prime meridian. Thus the length of a degree of longitude on the earth's surface is greatest at the latitude of the Equator and diminishes increasingly to zero at the poles.

MAP   The representation by means of symbols on a flat surface of the earth's surface and the distribution of phenomena thereon.

MAP PROJECTION   The method by which the curved surface of the earth is portrayed on a flat surface.

MAP SCALE   The ratio between a distance on a map and the actual distance it represents on the earth's

139

surface is known as the linear scale of the map. Area scales varying as the square of the linear scale are not generally shown on maps. Linear scales can be expressed as verbal statements or by graphs as well as by representative fractions.

NORTH POLE   The point at the northern extremity of the earth at which all longitude lines meet. The North Pole marks the northern end of the earth's axis of rotation.

OBLATE SPHEROID   A regular geometrical solid closely approximating the earth's true shape. This is a spheroid produced by the rotation of an ellipse about its shorter axis. The earth is only very slightly flattened in the vicinity of its poles and hence it has only minor oblateness.

OPTIMUM FLIGHT PATH   The "ideal" route for an aircraft between two airports. Generally the optimum flight path is regarded as that path which will require the minimum time to traverse it. Rarely does this least-time path coincide with the least-distance path, i.e., the great-circle route, because of the effect of wind.

POTENTIAL EVAPOTRANSPIRATION   This is a measure of the amount of moisture that could be evaporated and transpired by a full plant cover from the surface of the earth during a given time at a given place if there were never any shortage of water for such purposes.

POTENTIAL OF POPULATION   Potential of population measures at any given point the aggregate influence of an entire population or the aggregate accessibility to that entire population as it is geographically distributed. Maps of potential of population show the geographical variation in this spatially continuous macrogeographic "field quantity" by means of isolines, or isopotentials of population. (*See* Contour Line.) Potential of population and related measures have helped to make possible the macrogeographic study of important social and economic phenomena.

PRESSURE-PATTERN FLIGHT   This is the term used to include the various theoretical, mathematical, and practical methods to plan and actually navigate a minimum-time flight path for an aircraft through regions of varying atmospheric pressure.

RHUMB LINE   Any imaginary line on the earth's surface that cuts all meridians over which it passes at a constant angle.

SOUTH POLE   The point at the southern extremity of the earth at which all longitude lines meet. The South Pole marks the southern end of the earth's axis of rotation.

TOPOGRAPHY   This term is now generally used to refer to the details of the surface of a small area. In the United States, natural features are principally re-

141

ferred to, although sometimes here but especially in England, the term, topographic, includes both the natural and cultural features of an area. In ancient times, topography as the study of very small areas was contrasted with chorography and geography.

TOPOLOGY   A branch of mathematics concerned with spatial connectivities. The topologist especially studies geometric properties that remain unaltered despite certain transformations.

Index

147